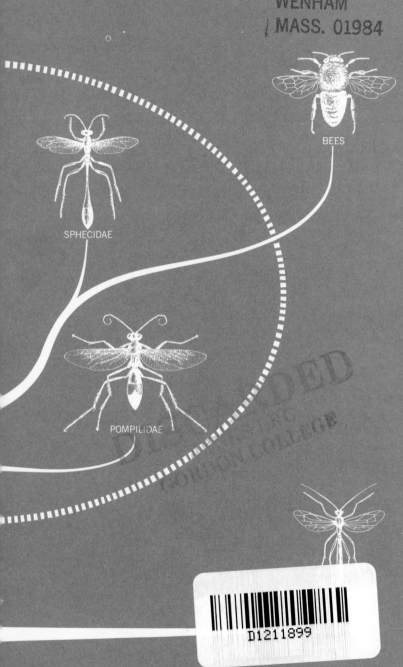

BEES

SPHECIDAE

POMPILIDAE

WASP FARM

The Natural History Press, publisher for The American Museum of Natural History, is a division of Doubleday & Company, Inc. Directed by a joint editorial board made up of members of the staff of both the Museum and Doubleday, the Natural History Press publishes books and periodicals in all branches of the life and earth sciences, including anthropology and astronomy. The Natural History Press has its editorial offices at The American Museum of Natural History, Central Park West at 79th Street, New York 24, New York, and its business offices at 501 Franklin Avenue, Garden City, New York.

WASP FARM

HOWARD ENSIGN EVANS

PUBLISHED FOR THE AMERICAN MUSEUM OF NATURAL HISTORY

The Natural History Press, Garden City, New York

Portions of this book are based on articles written by the author and previously published in *Natural History* magazine and *Nature Magazine*: "Adaptations of a Sand Wasp," from *Natural History* magazine, August-September 1959 and "Isodontia, A Grass-Carrying Wasp" from *Nature Magazine*, May 1959. Permission to use this material is hereby gratefully acknowledged.

All the photographs in this book were taken by the author. In addition to those published in *Natural History* magazine and *Nature Magazine*, three (numbers 5, 7, 15) have appeared in *Scientific American* and one (number 24) in *Audubon Magazine* and are reproduced here with their permission. The line illustrations were prepared by the Graphic Arts Division of The American Museum of Natural History.

Contents

Contents

Illustrations

WASP FARM

WASP FARM.

CHAPTER ONE

Wasp Farm and How It Came to Be

Readers who expect to find in this book a sequel to George Orwell's *Animal Farm* will be disappointed; it is about wasps, not about humans disguised as wasps, nor, I trust, about wasps imbued with human characteristics. Yet perhaps there is something Orwellian about the inexorability of wasps' lives, the tyranny of their instincts. Wasps share our planet but live in a different world. All about us they wind out their little lives, unaware that man is lord and master of the earth.

Ours is a world of vast panoramas, a world of jet transport, of atomic energy, of dawning world government or of vast devastation. Of what use are wasps? None, really. And yet they might save us. This is what I mean: so long as man is intent upon populating every square inch of the world and upon wringing every last drop of sustenance out of the earth, he is doomed. Even if things go well, and each of our great-grandchildren is blessed with a square yard of pavement, a roof, and all the comforts of twenty-first century living, what will have become of our heritage, of our ties with our origins? Will our great-grandchildren still read Thoreau?

> *I went to the woods because I wished to live deliberately,*
> *to front only the essential facts of life, and see if I could*
> *not learn what it had to teach . . .*

What is man? As a predator he is unrivaled but not unique; the world is full of lesser predators. It is as artist and scientist that he is unique, the only being able, in considerable measure, to understand and appreciate the world of which he is a part. And that world is fast slipping away from him—the real world, that is—to be replaced by an artificial world, built of concrete, steel, and chrome. Our eyes are upon the vastness of space, our dreams of other worlds, unexplored, unimaginable. Once again the thrill of the primeval, the challenge of unwarped nature! Yet our own tired planet still has its frontiers: my own back yard is full of them, full of creatures that put to shame the science-fiction writer's men of Mars. We would do well to spend less time reaching for stars, to value some things above comfort and the expansion of our economy. We would do well, now and then, to stretch out on the good earth with a notebook, camera, or sketch pad and chronicle the lives of some of our less self-important neighbors.

It was thoughts such as these that impelled us, a few years ago, to buy the eight acres of woods, fields, and bramble which became Wasp Farm. It needn't have been wasps, of course: beetles would have done nearly as well, or tardigrades. Tardigrades: there is a frontier for you. Have you ever seen one? I may not know where to find the distributor in my car; I may stumble over the laws of thermodynamics; but I have seen a tardigrade! Several, in fact. But wasps are my specialty. I won't try to unravel the various plots and subplots that resulted in the channeling of my interests into wasps. Suffice it to say there is (or ought to be) a specialist on everything. And there's a good deal to be said for wasps, as you will see.

Finding a place to establish Wasp Farm was not easy. We were newlyweds, in fact not yet married when we started our search. We soon found that the size of a mortgage is strictly determined by the size of one's salary, and in affairs of this sort a teacher's salary doesn't amount to much. We found, naturally, that people who want to sell a house don't advertise its potentialities for wasps, and these have to be sniffed out while one is pretending to inspect the well. The place we finally selected had a house which soon proved too small for our rapidly growing family, but which overlooked a broad panorama of woods, meadows, and lake. Its eight acres were rocky and mostly covered with bushes and brambles (but a good many wasps nest in brambles, and wild blackberries are delicious eating). One corner of the land had a patch of woods, mostly weed trees like poplars and locusts, but sufficient to support plenty of birds and insects and several patches of bloodroot. I suppose the thing that attracted us most was the sand pit in one corner of our land, for many wasps require sandy soil for digging their nests. The sand was not of very high quality, but sand is a scarce commodity in parts of upstate New York, and digger wasps can't afford to be choosy.

I use the past tense because, alas, we have since sold our eight acres of hilltop and been lured to Suburbia. But Wasp Farm is, after all, more an attitude than any particular piece of land. I doubt if our place had any more wasps than many a place of comparable size. To the people we bought it from it had been a chicken farm. To the present occupants, who knows? The wasp inhabitants have once again slipped back into obscurity, and it is all the same to them. But wherever we happen to be, wasps are king. I would hesitate to call our tiny chunk of Suburbia a farm; it is rather a base of operations for summer travel and winter reflection. This has been a long winter and our first winter away from Wasp Farm. From it emerged this book, a personal and slightly nostalgic account of wasps we have known and admired.

Wasps are not nearly the formidable creatures most people believe. It is true that the females of most species sting. The sting is a modification of the egg-laying apparatus and thus is not present in the males. The sting functions primarily to paralyze the insects or spiders on which wasps prey, so that they can be stored in a fresh but immobile state for their larvae to eat. Secondarily it can be used in defense, but most wasps have to be handled pretty roughly before they will sting. I often spend whole summers working with wasps without being stung a single time. In the social wasps, such as the hornets, yellow jackets, and common paper wasps, the sting has lost its importance in paralyzing the prey and serves primarily in defense of the colony. The nests of these wasps often occur around the haunts of man, and he who manhandles them learns a bitter lesson. But the social wasps make up only a small portion of the total kinds of wasps. Most wasps live solitary, unobtrusive lives, and to be stung by one is about as likely and as serious as being struck by a falling acorn: though for a few moments it is distinctly more painful.

Wasps, like other higher insects, go through four distinct stages during their lives: egg, larva, pupa, and adult. The eggs of wasps are whitish, very delicate and thin-shelled, and

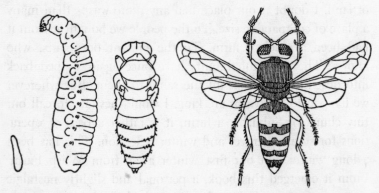

FIGURE 1. Egg, larva, pupa, and adult of a digger wasp (Bembix).

shaped somewhat like a slender sausage. They are laid in a small compartment of the nest called a cell; most wasps place a paralyzed insect or spider in the cell first, then lay the egg on that. The eggs of most wasps hatch in only two or three days, giving rise to a small grub-like larva which either begins to feed on the prey in the cell or has to be fed by the mother. The larva, too, is whitish, and has no legs or eyes; in a general way, it is like a sac with a mouth at one end and with mouthparts which fill up the sac at the expense of the food which has been placed in the cell. The larva grows very rapidly, and in a matter of five to ten days has reached its full size and begun to spin a cocoon in the cell. Although the behavior of the larva up to this point could hardly be simpler, suddenly some very complex behavior patterns make their appearance, for the cocoons of many wasps are very elaborate and require as much as two days of maneuvering and spinning. Some wasps incorporate sand grains into the wall of the cocoon and even prepare a series of rather complicated pores in the wall. Once the cocoon is complete, the larva becomes flaccid and dormant. Most solitary wasps spend the winter in this stage. Eventually, inside this rather amorphous sac, the form of the adult wasp begins to develop. Then one day the skin is cast off and the pupa appears, in much the form of the adult but whitish, with its appendages glued to the body and the wings in the form of small pads. Most wasps spend only a couple of weeks in this immobile pupal stage, then molt again and give rise to an adult wasp that eats its way out of the cocoon.

Adult male wasps usually emerge a few days before the females of the same species. They remain in the area where the females will shortly appear, and many of them fly about in characteristic prenuptial "dances." The females generally find a mate—or several mates—shortly after they emerge. The males live shorter lives than the females, and most of their lives are spent simply flying about or drinking nectar from flowers. With a few exceptions, they play no further role after they have mated. The females normally live several weeks (or, in the social wasps, as much as a full year). In these pages, I shall often refer to individual wasps as "she"; this is not from sentimentality, but because the wasps concerned are, in fact, females. The world of wasps, as well as of their relatives the bees and ants, is largely a female world. The workers of social wasps are all females, and the nests of social wasps and bees, and of all ants, contain nothing but females except during certain brief periods. Those who profess to find similarities between the societies of insects and those of men need to consider this very important difference—as well as many others. Personally, I have never felt that comparisons between humans and insects were very instructive: they are utterly different sorts of creatures which have followed separate paths of evolution for so long that we can't even postulate with much certainty when they had a common ancestor or what it was like.

Wasps, bees, ants, and a number of similar insects belong to a group known to science as the Hymenoptera, a name compounded from the Greek words for membrane wing. The many thousands of kinds of wasps are grouped into several complexes called families. This use of the word "family" is very different from the conventional one; it refers to a group of animals or plants which are related in the sense that they had a common ancestry a long while ago: for example, the swallow family or the lily family. The wasps considered in these pages belong to three families, and we may as well become acquainted with their scientific and common names right here.

(1) Pompilidae. Spider wasps or pompilids. Wasps with very long, usually spiny legs, all of which prey upon spiders. Most species are black in color, but some have red markings on the abdomen.

(2) Sphecidae. Digger wasps or sphecids. A very large group of wasps which show much variation in size, color, and general body form. The legs tend to be shorter than in spider

wasps and may or may not be spiny. Digger wasps prey upon a great variety of insects, some of them on spiders. Most of them dig in the soil, but some nest in hollow twigs and some build mud nests, the latter usually being called mud daubers.

(3) Vespidae. Mason wasps, paper wasps, yellow jackets, hornets, or simply vespids. Wasps with relatively short, smooth legs and nearly always banded with white or yellow markings. The wings fold lengthwise when the wasp is at rest. The major food consists of caterpillars. These wasps use mud or paper in building their nests.

Only a few of the more striking kinds of wasps have been given vernacular names: for example, the cicada killer, the black and yellow mud dauber. There are simply so many different species that it would be almost impossible to think up common names for them all. Personally, I see nothing objectionable to scientific names, and I have used these throughout this book. One needs only to remember that in a scientific name the group name (the name of the genus, or generic name) precedes the name of the species (just as the Chinese very logically put their surname before their given name). For instance, the common paper wasp in the northeastern states is Polistes fuscatus. In this case the species is fuscatus (the Latin word for blackish), the name of the genus to which it belongs Polistes (Greek for "founder of a city"). There are many other species of Polistes in the warmer parts of the world; for example, Polistes annularis is a common form in the Southeast, a larger species with a pale annulation on the base of the abdomen. To my mind, it doesn't help very much to call one the blackish paper wasp, the other the annulated paper wasp. The scientific names are euphonious, distinctive, and used to designate the species throughout the world.

Incidentally, there is no standard pronunciation for scientific names. I remember how shocked I once was to learn that the little wasp Oxybelus, which you will meet later in these pages, is called Oxy-bell'-us in Canada, though I have always heard it called Ox-ib'-el-us. Those who have had some Latin will want to pronounce scientific names as they would be in Latin; others may prefer to Anglicize them. At the end of each chapter I have indicated how I pronounce the names of the wasps in that chapter, but I don't insist that you pronounce them that way.

At the end of each chapter I have also listed a few references pertaining to the wasps discussed in that chapter. Really, quite a lot has been published on the behavior of wasps, and some of it makes fascinating reading. Wasps have been popular with naturalists for a long time, but especially since the times of the great French observer Jean Henri Fabre. Earlier workers were often content to watch a few individuals and write about them at considerable length, often not hesitating to postulate various "explanations" of what they observed. The work of recent students of wasps often makes less interesting reading, because these students tend to be more cautious, more objective, more concerned with precise description and less prone to theorizing. The more we learn, the more we realize how far we are from being able really to explain the behavior of wasps—or for that matter other animals, including man. The first step is the description of what an animal does under natural conditions. Such descriptions need to be detailed, carefully made, and carefully analyzed. The fact is that we don't know what most animals do in any real sense. We think of the honeybee as the most familiar of insects, yet there is still much to be learned about it. The behavior of our common paper wasp, Polistes, has been the source of much controversy between French and Italian entomologists. There are scores of relatively common wasps right in the eastern United States about which we know nothing at all.

Once all the *whats* have been answered, studies can proceed along one of two lines: along comparative lines, with the object of learning how certain behavior patterns evolved, or along experimental lines, with the object of learning the factors within the animal and in the environment which control behavior. We will say a little about these approaches, and make a few attempts at explaining the *hows* and *whys* of wasp behavior. But by and large students of wasps are still in the *what* stage, and will be for quite some time. So this book is mostly about what wasps do, chiefly what a few of the more individualistic denizens of Wasp Farm do. I think you'll agree that, even on this relatively unsophisticated level and in this quite unexotic situation, the study of wasps can be rewarding and exciting.

FOR FURTHER READING

Here are a few recent general books on animal behavior which I have found useful. They are technical books, but those by Scott and by Tinbergen are relatively easy going.

Carthy, J. D. 1958. An Introduction to the Behaviour of Invertebrates. George Allen & Unwin, London. 380 pp.

Roe, A., and Simpson, G. G., editors. 1958. Behavior and Evolution. Yale University Press, New Haven. 557 pp.

Scott, J. P. 1962. Animal Behavior. Doubleday Anchor Natural History Library. 281 pp.

Thorpe, W. H. 1956. Learning and Instinct in Animals. Harvard University Press, Cambridge, Mass. 493 pp.

Tinbergen, N. 1951. The Study of Instinct. Oxford University Press, London. 228 pp.

Olberg, G. 1959. Das Verhalten der Solitären Wespen Mitteleuropas (Vespidae, Pompilidae, Sphecidae). Deutscher Verlag der Wissenschaften, Berlin. 402 pp. This is a particularly fine recent book on wasp behavior. The text is in German, the captions to the illustrations in both German and English. The book is profusely illustrated with incredibly fine photographs, and a person interested in wasps who knows no German at all will find it worth perusing and even owning.

CHAPTER TWO

Of Spring and Spider Wasps

People write about spring as though it were something you could put your finger on, something you could wrap up in a bundle or in a sonnet. Perhaps it is in some places, but in central New York it has a way of sneaking up on one, all mixed up with winter, and just as soon as you notice it, it is slipping away, all mixed up with summer. Some say the first robins are a sure sign of spring, but don't believe it; the phoebes are less apt to be fooled by an early thaw. Spring peepers have a way of lifting one's hopes, but it may still be too early to put away the snow shovel. The first paper wasp may buzz around the bathroom almost any winter day when the sun's rays are warm enough to lure it from its winter's sleep among the rafters. But when the first yellow jackets and white-faced hornets begin to drone about on bright days in late May, you can be pretty sure it's spring. Or is it summer already?

The paper wasps and yellow jackets are "social" wasps, that is, they live in closely knit colonies where there is a division of labor. As wasps go, they are exceptional in many ways. The ones that appear in the spring are "queens" which are looking for a place to build a nest. They have mated the previous fall and have spent the winter sleeping in some protected place, the yellow jackets generally in an old log or woodpile, where, as a matter of fact, a good many of them perish. A few of the survivors will start paper nests and serve as mothers to a growing brood of daughters, ever ready to participate in a summer picnic. But the social wasps are the culmination of a long series of steps in evolution: the elite of the wasp world, if you like. We shall save them for a later chapter. The vast majority of wasps live solitary lives, and nearly all of these spend the winter very differently: as fully-grown, dormant larvae, generally in a cocoon in the soil or in a stem or mud nest. Some time in spring they transform into pupae; eventually the pupa darkens and the wasp rends the pupal skin, cuts its way out of the cocoon, and takes its place among the milling hordes of the insect world.

And milling hordes there are, even when the snows have barely left the scene. Have you ever wandered through the woods on a warm April day and marveled at the great numbers of insects that have suddenly sprung from what was, a few days before, a scene of frosty silence? Midges dance over a rotten log, small bees gather nectar from the bloodroots, and beetles creak in the litter. In late April, when the arbutus is in full bloom and the first trilliums opening, you may be lucky enough to find a great aggregation of that brilliant red beetle *Eros aurora*—literally "dawn love," and appropriately so, for these beetles live only a few days and, here at the dawn of the summer season, are concerned with little other than procreation. Why are they bright red? Perhaps, like the red center of a painted trillium, to delight the eye? One should perhaps be poetic in the spring, but is it unpoetic to admit that the function of a flower is to attract the insects that it needs for pollination? And that *Eros* is red for the same reason that the yellow jacket is banded with yellow: it is not good to eat (for birds, that is) and is advertising the fact.

Already, in the cool woods of April, with the leaves barely beginning to fill the canopy above, a solitary wasp is very

much in business. This is Priocnemis minorata, a hunter of
various spiders that run about the dried leaves and litter of
the spring woods. It is hardly a showy wasp, being black and
only half an inch long, but there is something exciting about
the flick of its wings in the timid April sunshine. The male
wasps flit about the ground searching for females or spend
their time taking nectar from willow catkins and the blossoms
of chokecherry. The females appear a bit later, and, like all
female wasps, are decidedly more businesslike. For years nothing much was known about this wasp, although it is common
enough in the northeastern United States and almost the only
wasp to appear so early in spring. A few years ago a student of
mine, Carl Yoshimoto, now a curator at the Bishop Museum
in Honolulu, devoted a great deal of patience and industry to
this wasp, and a good deal more is now known about it.

Yoshimoto found that the female Priocnemis minorata digs
a deep, vertical hole in the loam of the forest floor. This hole
is only a quarter of an inch in diameter and on the top is
rimmed with fresh soil, a bit like an ant's nest. The hole is
usually started from beneath fallen leaves, so that it is quite
invisible from above. Having finished the burrow, the female
spends much of her time hunting for spiders. She walks about
among the dried leaves, under loose bark, and in various
cracks and crannies, with her antennae in constant motion
and her wings continually flickering. Her quarry consists of
two genera of stocky, dull-colored spiders that overwinter as
adults and are active in the spring: Wadotes and Coras. Spider
wasps are persistent and effective hunters—perhaps you remember Pepsis (a relative of Priocnemis) stalking and stinging a tarantula in Walt Disney's *The Living Desert*. Yet spider
wasps often appear rather stupid to one who casually observes
them in nature. When, in their hunting activities, they detect
the presence of a spider, they become very excited and charge
about madly. Usually the spider bounds away with the wasp

in hot pursuit. The amazing thing is that the wasp, though apparently well endowed with the senses of sight and smell, often seems aware of only approximately where the spider is at a given moment, and may miss it again and again. Eventually, in many cases, the wasp succeeds in pouncing upon the spider and in bending her abdomen forward beneath her body, stinging it one or more times very quickly. These initial stings slow the spider down so the wasp can sting it once again, more slowly, on the underside of the front part of the body, where the nervous system is concentrated. In the case of Priocnemis, the resulting paralysis is deep and permanent, the spider remaining fresh but immobile for many days, thus assuring the wasp larva of a leisurely, succulent meal. Yoshimoto took several spiders from female wasps and kept them to see how long they would remain paralyzed but fresh; the longest period of time was thirty-three days (although normally it only takes the wasp larva a week to consume its spider!).

Having subdued a spider, Priocnemis may pause to clean herself and perhaps feed a bit on fluid exuding from the mouth or wounds of the spider. She then seizes the spider in her mandibles by the base of its hind legs and proceeds to walk backward to her nest. Always she proceeds in nearly a straight line with scarcely a pause and, so far as we know, without turning around to explore the terrain ahead. Apparently her first trips from the nest were used to memorize the details of the terrain, for she now seems to know precisely where to go, even though she is walking backward over a jumble of leaves and twigs and sometimes has to detour around rocks and stumps. Eventually she disappears beneath some dried leaves and in a moment has dragged the spider behind her into the hole.

Carl Yoshimoto spent many long hours watching different individuals carrying their spiders, and in this way was able to discover and mark many nests. After a period of time he dug out several of these to determine their structure. This was no easy matter. If you don't believe it, try tracing an irregular burrow only a quarter of an inch in diameter down through black, lumpy soil full of roots and stones. Many an excavation was partly or wholly unsuccessful, but there were enough successful ones so that we now feel confident that we understand some of the details of nest structure. The initial burrow goes down for about a foot, where it terminates in a small oval cell into which the first spider is placed and an egg laid upon it. This cell is then closed off, and over a period of days additional cells are constructed from short side-burrows successively back toward the entrance, so that there may eventually be as many as seven cells, each containing a spider. The wasp's egg is laid on the side of the spider's stout, rather soft abdomen, and when it hatches (in two or three days) the grub-like wasp larva which emerges begins to feed through the body wall on the viscera within. In a few days the abdomen is entirely gone and the larva turns to the front parts of the spider's body and hollows them out, leaving only the carapace and parts of the legs and mouthparts. Then, after only about a week of feeding, the larva spins a soft brown cocoon in which it remains dormant for nearly eleven months: until some one of the many factors which we collectively call "spring" triggers it into developing into first a pupa and then an adult wasp, ready to enact a script which is already largely codified in its nervous system.

By mid-June Priocnemis minorata has pretty much finished its nesting, though a few old females with tattered wings may still haunt the woods. In open places, about this time, a related wasp, Priocnemis cornica, is making its appearance. Less than half the size of minorata, cornica is a common inhabitant of gardens, gravel pits, and other areas of bare soil, but is rarely noticed by any but connoisseurs of wasps. I confess that cornica, tiny and dull-colored though it is, is one of my favorite spider wasps. The females are huntresses of many

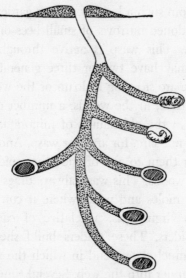

FIGURE 2. Nest of Priocnemis minorata in the loam of the forest floor. The top cell contains an egg, the next a larva, the bottom four cocoons.

kinds of tiny, mostly immature spiders. We know them to use at least fifteen different kinds of spiders. Once we saw a female carrying a rather unusual-looking object. We took it away from the wasp and found it to be nothing more than the cast skin of a spider! Once in a while, females of this species consume a spider themselves rather than take it to the nest for their offspring. A number of times we have seen two cornicas fighting over a spider. Once we saw a cornica female steal a spider from a different species of spider wasp; this wasp had left the spider on the ground while she dug her nest, and by the time she discovered her loss the Priocnemis had carried the spider many feet away. The nests of cornica are very much like those of minorata, but the cells are usually constructed from some pre-existing hole in the ground rather than one specially dug for that purpose. Often the abandoned, vertical tube of a tiger beetle larva is employed, and numerous cells may be built from such a burrow. In our garden, cornica nests mostly in abandoned burrows of small bees or in holes made by earthworms. This wasp is active throughout the entire summer, and may have two or three generations while the minorata larvae are sleeping in loam of the woods.

In the meantime, in the woods, a number of other species have appeared in the old haunts of minorata. The Wadotes spiders are still not safe, for another wasp, Anoplius carolinus, seems to prefer them to any of the other spiders which now abound in the woods. This wasp always drags its spiders into old burrows of moles and mice, where it constructs its nest-cells. Anoplius virginiensis, a relative of carolinus, attacks Agelenopsis spiders. These spiders build sheet-webs in the grass, with a funnel at one end in which the spider waits for an insect to blunder into the web. Several times we have seen Anoplius virginiensis deliberately land in such webs and chase the spider about. These webs contain no adhesive threads, and the wasps are adept at running over them without becoming entangled. When attacked by Anoplius, the Agelenopsis usually leaves its funnel-web and runs off through the woods. We have several times seen the spider make good its escape, and have yet to see the wasp succeed in catching one. But succeed it does, sometimes, for the nests of virginiensis which we have found are almost always provisioned with Agelenopsis. The nest-cells of this wasp are prepared in series in old beetle burrows in soft wood.

One of the most distinctive wasps in the summer woods is a small one with twice-banded wings, Dipogon sayi. Dipogon literally means "two beards," an appropriate name for this wasp, which has two tufts of long bristles which curve up toward the mouth from below. Dipogon, like Anoplius virginiensis, nests in pre-existing burrows in wood, where it makes a series of cells. The beards of Dipogon are reported by some European and Japanese workers to be used for collecting spiders' webs which are made into a pad and used for closing off the nest-cells. Dipogon sayi doesn't seem to collect spiders' webs, but we have seen females picking up pieces of earth and wood fragments and carrying them to the nest. The partitions between the cells are composed of firmly compacted, fine-grained earth or rotted plant materials, perhaps with the addition of water or plant resins. The space between the last cell partition and the opening of the burrow is filled by the wasp with a plug consisting of loosely compacted materials such as sand grains, lumps of earth, bits of grass, leaves, moss, wood chips, seeds, dead insects, and even the droppings of caterpillars. Apparently the wasp picks up whatever she can

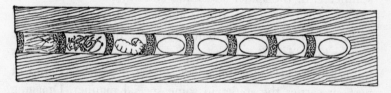

FIGURE 3. Nest of Dipogon sayi in a trap nest. The inner five cells contain cocoons.

find on the ground around the nest. One individual we studied was quite an entomologist: the filling of her nest contained a dismembered beetle, the head of a fly, the heads of two carpenter ants, and about twenty whole, dried ants. Probably this wasp had found an ant nest nearby which had a number of dead ants outside the entrance. Most plugs have a stratified appearance, layers of different materials succeeding one another as the wasp discovers different sources of fill in the vicinity of the nest.

Dipogon sayi is a rather easy wasp to study. One can take short sections of sumac twigs, bore a hole in one end, and tie these in various trees in the woods. Many different wasps, bees, and other insects make use of these borings, including Dipogon sayi. We have taken about twenty nests of the species in this way without making any special effort. By saturating various wooded areas with "trap nests" of this type, two biologists at the University of Wisconsin were able to collect 221 nests of Dipogon sayi. Most finished nests contain from three to six cells, but these workers found one nest with thirteen cells. As usual among spider wasps, each cell contains a single paralyzed spider. By far the majority of spiders taken by sayi are small, dull-colored crab spiders of the genus Xysticus, which are common in litter and low vegetation of the summer woods. Incidentally, in keeping with its rugged individualism, Dipogon carries its spider not backwards like most spider wasps or forwards like a few; instead, the wasp grasps the spinnerets of the spider and walks sideways!

One of the surprising things about spider wasps is that all of them are similar in so many ways, yet most of them have certain individualities: a given species or group of species preys upon a particular kind of spider, makes a particular kind of nest, or carries the spider in some special manner. Dragging the spider backward, as most of them do, seems an awkward way to proceed: for one thing, they can't see where they are going. But to walk forward involves difficulties, too. Since each spider has to be sufficient to feed a wasp larva, it must approximate the wasp in size or actually be a little larger. So, a wasp walking forward with a spider in its mandibles as big as itself is not apt to see much either, and has the additional possibility of stumbling over its huge burden. The species that do proceed forward have solved these problems in various ways. Some of them drag the spider backward up a plant and then fly forward with it, letting the spider dangle from the mandibles. Of course they lose altitude rapidly in most cases, but at least they have gained a few feet. Other kinds of spider wasps grasp either the front or tail end of the spider and strad-

dle it, the body of the spider bouncing along beneath that of
the wasp. But spiders have long legs, and this might prove an
awkward arrangement without an odd bit of behavior that
accompanies such a mode of transport: The wasp neatly snips
off the legs of the spider at the base, at a point where they
normally break off readily and do not bleed appreciably. By
doing this, the wasp can walk rapidly forward without danger
of falling over the legs of its prey.

One particular spider wasp has received a good deal of pub-
licity for its remarkable way of carrying the spider. The late
Professor James G. Needham of Cornell University was the
first to draw attention to this wasp. About fifty years ago,
Professor Needham watched one flying over the surface of a
quiet stream near Cornell dragging a large spider over the
surface film, "leaving a wake that is a miniature of that of a
passing steamer." By using the waterway, the wasp was presumably able to avoid the dense vegetation of the stream-
side as well as to utilize the buoyancy of the water. Some
years later, Phil Rau, the Missouri schoolteacher who spent
much of his life chronicling the lives of wasps, made some
similar observations in Missouri and also quoted a fisherman
who watched a wasp carry four spiders in this manner to its
nest somewhere in a railroad trestle. Rau characterized this
behavior as "highly intelligent," and many a subsequent writer
has praised this wasp either for its intelligence or for its remarkable instincts, depending upon his bias. I remember reading about it in Edwin Way Teale's *Boys' Book of Insects*
when that book first came out in 1939. The curious thing is
that until 1949 the identity of the wasp remained a mystery.
Rau had failed to identify it, and Needham had given it the
name of a nonexistent species, so for years and years it remained simply "that mysterious nautical wasp."

Now, taxonomists—persons who study classification and
identification—are not often given credit for making any very
startling discoveries. But it was a taxonomist (myself, in fact)

who solved this particular riddle. When I was a graduate student, I made a study of this particular group of wasps, basing it in the usual manner on the specimens in the collections of various museums. In the Smithsonian Institution in Washington, D.C. I discovered a wasp which I readily identified as Anoplius depressipes (literally, "flat-footed"). On the same pin with the wasp was a large water spider of the genus Dolomedes and also the note: "taken while towing a spider up a canal." In Pittsburgh's Carnegie Museum was another specimen of this same wasp, also pinned with a Dolomedes and bearing a very similar note: "Wasp was dragging spider over water to shore. Spider in contact with water." The two wasps and accompanying notes were taken by different persons in very different localities. It seemed almost certain that here was the unknown wasp of Needham and of Rau.

But there is more to the story. In 1922 A. N. Caudell, a well-known government entomologist, wrote a short paper entitled "A Diving Wasp." Caudell's wasp was seen to crawl beneath the surface of still water and walk about on the bottom; it was also adept at walking on the surface film in the manner of a water strider. Caudell provided a name for the wasp, but it was incorrect. I was able to find the specimen he worked with in the Smithsonian Institution and it was, of course, Anoplius depressipes. Now this wasp is, as a matter of fact, "flat-footed," and uniquely so. The outer parts of its legs are distinctly flattened, the sides of the flattened portion fringed with short hairs. Obviously, this is an adaptation for walking on the surface film, a necessity for a wasp which pursues spiders which spend much of their lives on the surface of water. Dolomedes spiders dive when frightened, and it is obviously useful to the wasp to be able to dive, too. And, since depressipes is now known to nest in holes along the banks of ponds and streams, what could be more natural than that this well-adapted wasp should raft its spiders over the water?

A few years ago my indefatigable assistant, Carl Yoshimoto, saw an Anoplius depressipes sting a Dolomedes spider on an equisetum growing in sand along water. The spider fell to the sand and the Anoplius began to drag it backward in the manner common to so many spider wasps. Then it turned about and began to buzz its wings, dragging the spider forward over the sand in exactly the same manner as it does over the water! Somehow this behavior no longer seemed so remarkable, as it seemed obvious that depressipes differed less from other spider wasps than had been supposed. Knowledge of the nest of depressipes was achieved through the efforts of William Guild, director of the Science Museum in St. Petersburg, Florida, who watched a wasp rafting a spider in Massachusetts a few years ago and wrote me a letter about it. He saw the wasp carry its spider into a knothole in an old telephone pole which was lying in the water. When he found out that I was much interested, he got a cross-cut saw (noble soul!) and with a helper sawed out a great chunk of the telephone pole and mailed it to me. In the knothole I found two cells of the

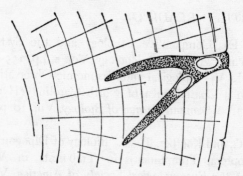

FIGURE 4. Nest of Anoplius depressipes in a decayed portion around a knot in a telephone pole. Both cells contain cocoons.

wasp, from each of which I reared an Anoplius depressipes. With this, the final piece of the puzzle was in place, and this wasp emerged as quite the most individualistic of any I know. Whether or not Phil Rau was justified in calling it "highly intelligent" I shall let you judge for yourself.

CAST OF CHARACTERS

Priocnemis minorata: Pry-ok-nee′-miss (from the Greek *prion*, saw, plus *cneme*, leg, a reference to the saw teeth on the hind legs of this wasp) min-o-rate′-a (from the Latin *minor*, smaller).

Priocnemis cornica: corn′-ik-a (Latin meaning horned, perhaps also an allusion to the teeth on the hind legs).

Anoplius carolinus: An-oh′-plee-us (from the Greek *anoplos*, without armor, referring to the fact that some species have relatively few spines on the legs) care-oh-line′-us (pertaining to Carolina, where this wasp was first discovered).

Anoplius virginiensis: vir-gin-ee-en′-sis (Latin, living in Virginia).

Anoplius depressipes: dee-press′-ip-eez (Latin, *depressus*, pressed down, plus *pes*, foot, a reference to the flattened legs).

Dipogon sayi: Die-poh′-gon (Greek *dis*, double, plus *pogon*, beard, a reference to the two sets of bristle on the mouthparts) say′-eye (of Thomas Say, an early American entomologist).

FOR FURTHER READING

Evans, H. E. "Comparative Ethology and the Systematics of Spider Wasps." *Systematic Zoology*, Vol. 2, pp. 155–72 (1953).

Krombein, K. V. "Biological and Taxonomic Observations on the Wasps in a Coastal Area of North Carolina (Hymenoptera: Aculeata)." *Wasmann Journal of Biology*, Vol. 10, pp. 257–341 (1953).

Medler, J. T., and Koerber, T. W. "Biology of Dipogon sayi Banks (Hymenoptera, Pompilidae) in Trap-nests in Wisconsin." *Annals of the Entomological Society of America*, Vol. 50, pp. 621–25 (1957).

Rau, P. and N. *Wasp Studies Afield*. Princeton, N. J.: Princeton University Press (1918).

Yoshimoto, C. M. "A Study of the Biology of Priocnemis minorata Banks (Hymenoptera, Pompilidae)." *Bulletin of the Brooklyn Entomological Society*, Vol. 49, pp. 130–38 (1954).

CHAPTER THREE

The Case of the Missing Egg

One of the best features of Wasp Farm is that here I can perform all necessary observations and operations far from curious eyes. Here wasp-watching is the order of the day, and our children are growing up, I'm sure, thinking that everybody watches wasps. Out in the world, I'm afraid, this is far from the truth. I remember once when I was a student and was visiting my mother, I discovered a wonderful nesting site for digger wasps in a neighboring lot. As I lay there in the dust in the hot sun scribbling notes on a pad, two of the more staid ladies of the neighborhood strolled by, slightly goggle-eyed. I suppose they had some comments on what college had done to Mrs. Evans' boy.

I remember that particular incident very well because it was my first real acquaintance with a small blue spider wasp called Evagetes parvus. I had seen Evagetes before and was aware that there was something odd about it. The females didn't seem to hunt spiders and bury them in nests in the soil as proper spider wasps should; rather they spent their time walking over the sand with their antennae tapping the soil like divining rods. Now and then one would see an Evagetes lurking about when another spider wasp was nesting. What were they up to? That particular afternoon gave me part of the answer.

In a small bare place an Anoplius marginatus had dug a nest, while an Evagetes parvus perched stark still on a grass blade about a foot away. After a while the Anoplius went off and came back dragging a spider which she had stung earlier and hidden in the crotch of a weed (as this species commonly does). She proceeded to leave the spider at the edge of the burrow, go inside, then pull in the spider by the spinnerets. During this episode the Evagetes moved about a bit, but still kept her distance. Soon I could see the Anoplius down in the burrow scraping sand from the sides of the burrow and packing it in place with blows of the tip of her abdomen. Suddenly the Evagetes seemed unable to contain herself any longer and rushed into the partially filled burrow. The Anoplius popped out and stood there as if not quite sure what had hit her; then, in a moment, she resumed her filling, leaving the Evagetes inside the nest. How the two managed to pass in the narrow burrow I have no idea. More surprising, even, was the Anoplius' apparent unawareness of what was going on. If Evagetes was a parasite of Anoplius, as seemed likely, how did it happen that Anoplius had never evolved means of attacking, avoiding, or at least recognizing its enemy?

In a few moments the Anoplius had finished filling her burrow and left. Needless to say I was as eager to get into the nest as the Evagetes had been. What was going on down in the cell? I carefully cut away the soil with my pocketknife and in a short while uncovered the cell. The Evagetes was sitting quietly on top of the spider and allowed herself to be picked up with my forceps. The spider appeared to bear no egg, and later, even with a hand lens, I could discover no egg on the spider. It seemed to me that the mouthparts of the Evagetes were suspiciously moist, but it was hard to be sure that this was significant. Had the Evagetes eaten the Anoplius egg? What would the actions of the Evagetes have been had

I not disturbed her? It would take other hot days lying in the dust to find that out.

It wasn't until several years later, when I was an instructor at a midwestern college, that I was able to work out the rest of the story. Usually spider wasps are scarce enough so that one has to put together little pieces of information gleaned here and there. For a change I found myself in an area where they were abundant enough so that I could really go to work on them. Most of my spare hours were spent along a delightful little spring-fed stream that meandered through some sand hills. It was called Blackjack Creek, not, I think, because of any tales of thugs or bandits associated with it, but simply because the dominant trees were blackjack oaks. The stream valley supported a rich variety of plant life and an abundance of insects of many kinds; digger wasps had plenty of prey available and an infinity of fine sand of varying moisture and consistency. Indeed, I have never in my life seen a place so teeming with wasps. I wish I could have taken Blackjack Creek with me when I left the area. I'm sure the local residents don't fully appreciate it!

One of the dominant wasps here was Anoplius apiculatus, a pretty little red-and-black sprite covered with glaucous pubescence. With the help of two graduate students, I was able to learn a great deal about apiculatus. The females hunted for spiders in moist sand along the stream; here they found a very common gray sand-spider, Arctosa littoralis, which provided the sole prey of the species. Having captured and stung a spider, they dragged it up into somewhat drier sand away from the stream and left it on the ground while they dug a short nest. After the nest was well started, they always moved their spider to the entrance or even just inside the entrance, where it became partly or wholly covered with sand. This may have been an adaptation for avoiding the attacks of certain flies which were common in the area. These flies normally deposit small, live larvae on the spiders, and the maggots proceed to develop, after the spider has been placed in the cell, at the expense of the wasp egg and the spider. Although Anoplius apiculatus may have evolved this particular mechanism for escaping parasitic flies, it proved to be, like Anoplius marginatus, quite inept at avoiding (or even recognizing) its sycophant cousin, Evagetes.

The Evagetes in this area was a glossy blue species which was slightly larger than parvus and was called mohave. We soon discovered that it behaved in much the same way as parvus. The females were commonly seen walking over the sand with their antennae in rapid motion. One day we saw one come across a partially completed nest of Anoplius apiculatus, apparently by accident. The Evagetes entered the nest and then came out quickly and walked about two feet away, where she turned, facing the nest, and remained completely motionless for some time. Meanwhile the Anoplius finished her nest, extricated her spider from beneath the pile of sand at the entrance, and placed it in the cell and laid her egg upon it. At this point the Evagetes suddenly came to life and rushed into the burrow. For fully five minutes the two wasps were in the burrow together, and I would have given a great deal to know what was going on. Eventually the Anoplius came tearing out, as though pursued by demons, but in a moment she began to fill the nest in the normal manner. This time I realized that if I wanted to learn the full story I would have to practice a bit more self-control than before, so I patiently awaited further events. The Anoplius finished her filling in about ten minutes, scraped a little sand here and there over the entrance, then flew off. Another five minutes elapsed, when suddenly the Evagetes pushed her way out through the sand, leaving a small hole which she did not attempt to cover.

At last I was free to dig out the nest. I found it to be a typical apiculatus nest, with the spider in the usual position.

But the apiculatus egg is whitish, about 1.5 millimeters in length, and is always laid obliquely on the side of the spider's abdomen. This spider bore an egg transversely across the back of its abdomen; the egg was only one millimeter long and somewhat cream-colored, while the larva which hatched from it in two days was decidedly more pinkish than that of Anoplius apiculatus. This was obviously the work of Evagetes, which had consumed the Anoplius egg and laid her own on the spider. The larva fed for five days on the spider, then spun its cocoon. Nineteen days later an adult female Evagetes mohave emerged from the cocoon, thus removing any possible doubt as to what had transpired.

In the meantime we were gathering further data. I remembered reading that the Swedish naturalist Gottfrid Adlerz had once studied a European Evagetes with considerable success by placing the Evagetes in a glass tube with the egg and spider of the host wasp. Consequently we went back to Blackjack Creek armed with a very elaborate piece of scientific equipment: an empty peanut butter jar. In the bottom of the jar we placed a layer of sand. We then waited until we found an Anoplius apiculatus nesting, dug up the nest, and placed the spider bearing the Anoplius egg in a small, artificial cell in the sand of our jar, against the wall where we could see it. It was a simple matter to capture a female Evagetes mohave and place her in the jar, but when our Evagetes proceeded to spend all her time trying to escape from the jar we became discouraged. However, after about ten minutes she accidentally dug into the cell (which we had put just beneath the surface of the sand). Suddenly she became a different wasp, focusing her attention on the spider and the egg it bore and no longer concerned with escaping. For half a minute she ran her antennae over the spider; then she grasped the Anoplius egg firmly in her mandibles and worked it back and forth until it came loose. Then, still holding the egg in her mandibles,

she straddled the spider and began rubbing the tip of her
abdomen back and forth across the spider's abdomen, eventually laying her egg in the same position as in the preceding
example. Having done this, she shortly left the cell and once
again spent her time trying to escape from the jar. Spider and
egg were removed to a rearing tin, where a male Evagetes was
produced twenty-two days later.

Delighted with our success, we repeated our experiment
several more times. In some cases the Evagetes seemed able
to detect the whereabouts of the cell, presumably by odor,
and this led us to conclude that females sometimes find completed nests in nature and dig into them after the Anoplius
has left. We found that the Evagetes normally chewed up the
Anoplius egg, rather than simply holding it. On one occasion
we used a spider from a preceding experiment which already
bore an Evagetes egg. A female Evagetes (not the same one
that had laid the egg) treated it in the usual manner, chewing up the egg and laying another in the same place. I suppose
it must rarely occur in nature that an Evagetes enters a nest
which has already been invaded by another Evagetes! Other
experiments established that Evagetes will not lay her egg on a
paralyzed spider which does not bear an egg. Nor will Evagetes
touch a spider which bears an Anoplius egg which has already hatched into a small larva. We discovered, too, that if
the spider has already begun to recover from paralysis (as
sometimes happens, since the sting of Anoplius apiculatus
produces only temporary paralysis), the Evagetes will actually
sting the spider in the cell before laying her egg.

Species of Evagetes occur throughout much of the world,
although until recently they have not been recognized as belonging together and to a genus parasitic on other spider
wasps. All of the species have short, thick antennae which
are slightly flattened and covered with an abundance of small
sense organs. Doubtless these play an important role in finding

the nest of their host. In many details of structure and behavior, Evagetes is very much like Anoplius and related groups. There seems little doubt that Evagetes evolved from

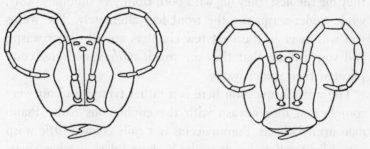

FIGURE 5. Heads of Anoplius marginatus (*left*) and its parasite, Evagetes parvus (*right*). The rather thick antennae of Evagetes apparently serve to "smell out" the nests of Anoplius in the soil.

Anoplius or a related genus. Perhaps the original ancestral Evagetes merely stole an occasional spider in the manner of Priocnemis cornica, mentioned in the last chapter. As this proved a successful way of life, the processes of evolution gradually molded a more perfect thief-parasite (or cleptoparasite, from the Greek word *kleptes*, thief). Some genera of spider wasps have even gone far beyond Evagetes in their adaptations of structure and behavior which render them effective cleptoparasites. But these are a long story in themselves.

I confess that I have only rarely seen Evagetes on Wasp Farm, and all of my work on it has been done elsewhere. But Wasp Farm has many times been the locale of a similar tale of subterfuge involving very different actors. These wasps belong to an entirely different group, the Sphecidae or true digger wasps. True digger wasps are not unrelated to spider wasps, but they show a good many advances in structural adaptation as well as generally more elaborate types of behavior. For example, all but a few primitive ones make the nest before catching their prey, and most of them prey on smaller insects and provide several of them per nest. When they dig the nest, they dig with both front legs simultaneously, while spider wasps use the front legs alternately. The wasps you will meet in the next few chapters are all digger wasps, and you will see that they are much more varied and complicated than spider wasps.

The wasp in question here is a rather typical and not very complicated digger wasp with the euphonious name Psammaecius nebulosus. Psammaecius is a gaily colored little wasp with bright yellow bands on its back and dark patches on its wings. Somehow it never manages to become very common on Wasp Farm, but every year we have a few of them nesting in our sand pit. Psammaecius is a hunter of treehoppers, very common insects which suck juices from trees and shrubs and sometimes injure plants by cutting slits in stems in which to lay their eggs. Treehoppers are remarkable for having a large shield which covers most of their back and even their wings. This shield is very differently shaped in different treehoppers. The buffalo treehopper, which is sometimes a pest in young fruit orchards, has the shield modified to form a pair of horns in front and a strong keel behind. Another common form has the shield shaped exactly like a thorn, and these insects sit motionless on stems and do indeed resemble thorns. Tropical treehoppers are often most bizarre, some having the dorsal shield very high and flat and patterned with bright colors like tropical fish, others having the shield in the shape of an ant's body or simply a series of lumps which look like nothing in particular. Immature treehoppers have no dorsal shield, but instead the body is covered with large, prickling spines. Psammaecius preys upon a wide variety of treehoppers, both adult and immature, including the buffalo treehopper and the thornlike ones, which obviously don't deceive the wasps.

Psammaecius makes a simple, shallow nest very much like that of many of the spider wasps. The nest is rarely started on bare sand, but rather under a leaf or stick or in a crevice between stones. Once it is completed, the wasp scrapes sand over the entrance and takes off to find a treehopper. She flies back to the nest with the hopper tucked somewhat awkwardly beneath her body, held tightly by her middle legs. She then scrapes open the nest entrance with her front legs and takes the prey directly to the cell. Then she leaves again promptly and repeats the performance. After a few hours the cell has been filled tightly with treehoppers, all of which are packed head-in, upside-down. It may take anywhere from eight to eighteen treehoppers, depending upon how large they are, to fill the cell. When the last hopper is in place, the wasp lays her egg on it along the leg-bases on one side. Then she closes off the cell. Sometimes a wasp prepares two or even three cells from the same burrow, sometimes only one, depending, perhaps, on how good the hunting has been.

Psammaecius strikes one as an industrious and efficient wasp, not the sort that would put up with the shenanigans of an Evagetes. Nevertheless it is rather commonly attacked by a cleptoparasite which has some points in common with Evagetes. At least it has short, thick antennae which it uses in much the same way: to locate the nests of its host by

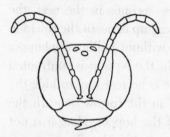 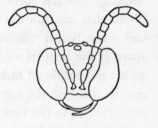

FIGURE 6. Heads of Psammaecius nebulosus (*left*) and its parasite, Nysson tuberculatus (*right*). Note the slanting eyes and slightly thicker antennae of the parasite.

"smelling them out" in the soil. But Nysson tuberculatus is very different in appearance from Evagetes, being related in fact to its host Psammaecius. The female Nysson spends most of her time walking and flying over the sand examining various holes. If she discovers a Psammaecius digging a nest or carrying in prey she lurks about until the Psammaecius leaves. At other times she apparently is able to detect the nest even though the wasp is away. In either case she digs quickly through the barrier at the entrance, stays in the cell only a few seconds, then comes out and closes the entrance neatly and in very much the same manner as the Psammaecius might do it. The whole operation occurs so quickly that the Psammaecius is unlikely to catch her in the act and, on returning to the nest, seems quite unaware that anything is amiss. She goes right on filling the cell, lays her egg, then closes the cell. As a matter of fact nothing much is amiss. Dig out the cell and you will find everything in order; the treehoppers lie in their proper arrangement and the Psammaecius egg rests in its usual position on the top one.

But the Nysson was not just checking up on the Psammaecius, you may be sure. The Nysson has laid her own rather small egg somewhere in the cell; the problem is to find it. If the treehoppers are adults, the place to look is on the underside of the dorsal shield of one of the bottom hoppers. Although she has spent only a few seconds in the nest, the Nysson has had time to thrust the egg up beneath the shield in such a way that it is quite invisible without pulling the hopper apart. If the hoppers are all nymphs the Nysson is confronted with a more difficult task, for there is no real way to hide the egg. In this case the egg is placed in the furrow beneath the beak, that is, in the neck region of the hopper. Here it is not so well concealed, but in my experience the Psammaecius does not detect it, or at least does not react to it. Apparently the egg-laying behavior of Nysson is sufficiently plastic so that the female can make use of the best available hiding place on the treehopper.

The cell thus contains two eggs, the small, hidden Nysson egg and the larger Psammaecius egg on top of the pile. Surely the larger egg will give rise to the larger and stronger larva! But put the contents of such a cell in a rearing tin, and you will invariably rear a Nysson! What has happened? Here is how Edward G. Reinhard puts it in his delightful book *The Witchery of Wasps*. (Reinhard was working with a different Psammaecius and a different Nysson, but the details can scarcely differ materially.)

"As the hours pass two eggs are developing side by side, to nurture larvae destined for deadly strife. The parasite is born in advance of its host. The young interloper takes a little Ceresa [treehopper] juice for sustenance, then without much delay advances toward its unborn nursery-mate. The larva, son of the parasite, moves about the nest, toddles as it were across the floor, clambers over the bodies of the tree-hoppers to where the helpless child of [Psammaecius] lies immaculate and inviolate, awaiting deliverance.

"The larva, a short, stout, large-headed, grim-looking ogre, has no tender caresses to bestow. His mouth is fitted with a pair of thin hooks which are sharp and curved like the fangs of a viper. The greeting is murderous and merciless. Cruel fangs pierce the egg and deprive the defenseless infant of life and inheritance. The parasite usurper disposes of its rival. A cannibal is now sole master of the spoils."

Reading Reinhard's colorful prose almost makes one want to institute some sort of eradication program against clepto-parasites! Nysson is indeed well adapted as a parasite of Psammaecius, though it attacks no other digger wasps. The structure of Nysson suggests that it is related to Psammaecius and probably evolved from a common ancestor, just as Evagetes probably shared a common ancestry with Anoplius.

Nysson is of course a more advanced type of parasite than
Evagetes, since it has developed a special manner of laying
the egg and specializations in the behavior of the larva. A
few other cleptoparasitic wasps are known, and they tend to
follow either the Nysson pattern or the Evagetes pattern.
Among the bees there are some excellent examples of cleptoparasitism. The common leaf-cutter bee, Megachile, is attacked by a related genus, Coelioxys, which slips into the nest
while the Megachile is away in much the manner of Nysson.
The Coelioxys plunges its egg into the pollen mass in the cell,
and the Megachile finishes filling the cell and then lays its egg
on top. The rest of the story you can guess. Some of the most
remarkable cases of cleptoparasitism occur among the ants,
culminating in species of ants which can no longer exist except
by making slaves of ants of related genera. But these, again,
are a long story in themselves.

On the other hand, there are many wasps, bees, and ants
which have no cleptoparasites at all. Why should Psammaecius, a rather inconspicuous and unremarkable wasp, be
perpetually plagued by its delinquent cousin Nysson, when so
many other wasps live in harmony with their relatives? Perhaps that is like asking why some people have trouble with
their in-laws and some do not. The web of evolution is complicated enough without asking why certain strands divide,
develop, or die out. And if man had not developed from one
such strand there would be no one around to ask such
questions!

CAST OF CHARACTERS

Evagetes parvus: Ev-a-gee'-teez (Greek *eu*, very, plus *agetos*, ad-
    mirable) par'-vus (Latin, small).
Evagetes mohave: moe-hah'-vee (a tribe of Indians of southwest-
    ern U.S.; this wasp was described first from Arizona).

Anoplius marginatus: An-oh'-plee-us (from the Greek *anoplos*, without armor) mar-gin-ate'-us (Latin, margined, a reference to the fact that the wings have a dark margin).

Anoplius apiculatus: a-pick-you-late'-us (Latin, small-pointed, perhaps with reference to the tip of the abdomen with its sting).

Psammaecius nebulosus: Sam-ee'-see-us (Greek *psammos*, sand, plus *oikos*, dwelling) neb-you-low'-sus (Latin, cloudy, a reference to the dark patches on the wings of this wasp).

Nysson tuberculatus: Niss'-on (Greek, one who pricks) too-burr-cu-late'-us (Latin, tuberculate, referring to paired spines on the middle of the body of this wasp).

FOR FURTHER READING

Evans, H. E., Lin, C. S., and Yoshimoto, C. M. "A Biological Study of Anoplius apiculatus autumnalis (Banks) and Its Parasite, Evagetes mohave (Banks) (Hymenoptera, Pompilidae)." *Journal of the New York Entomological Society*, Vol. 61, pp. 61–78 (1953).

Reinhard, E. G. *The Witchery of Wasps*. New York: The Century Company (1929).

Wheeler, W. M. "The Parasite Aculeata, a Study in Evolution." *Proceedings of the American Philosophical Society*, Vol. 58, pp. 1–40 (1919).

CHAPTER FOUR

Stinkbugs for Dinner

Have you ever eaten a stinkbug? Most people haven't, deliberately, but do you recall that rather strange-tasting raspberry that you spit out so quickly? Everyone unwittingly consumes an appalling number of insects in the course of a lifetime, but stinkbugs fortunately rarely get beyond the mouth without being blown out vehemently and with appropriate invective. Doubtless they taste no better to birds and other insectivorous creatures, most of which quickly learn to look for choicer morsels to feed upon. The "stink" is actually a repugnant chemical which is discharged from glands on the back of the young stinkbug. When the bug reaches adulthood and acquires wings, the gland openings (which would be covered by the wings) conveniently move to the underside of the bug. Most kinds have an "evaporation plate" outside the opening of the gland; this permits the chemical to evaporate slowly and enshroud the bug in protective fumes. Some bugs are actually able to squirt the fluid a considerable distance. A few years ago, while living in Mexico, we kept a large one for several days as a pet (it was one of the most beautiful insects I have ever known, black with a pattern of brilliant white and red lines). When our daughter (who was three at the time) sees our Kodachrome of the bug, she still remembers with disgust how effectively our pet could discharge its repugnant fluids when disturbed by small fingers.

There is not much question that the glands of stinkbugs have evolved as a means of protection against predators. It is a curious fact, though, that three quite unrelated groups of digger wasps not only prey on stinkbugs, but will take nothing else. They not only are not repelled by the odor and taste, but it is possible that they find certain advantages in using stinkbugs: they may be easier to find by smell than most other insects. Of course, one could argue that the adult wasps don't eat the stinkbugs themselves but feed on the nectar of their favorite flowers; they stock their nests with stinkbugs for their larvae. Since stinkbugs are easy to find, the wasps have more time to sip nectar, while the poor larvae have to eat stinkbugs or starve.

One genus of stinkbug predators, Paranysson, is African, but the other two, Bicyrtes and Astata, have a number of common species in North America. Both of them nest on Wasp Farm, and in fact they both nest at about the same time (late July and early August) and often use the same kinds of stinkbugs. But therein the resemblance ends; it would be hard to imagine two more dissimilar wasps than Bicyrtes ventralis and Astata unicolor: Bicyrtes sleek, brightly patterned, and businesslike, Astata chubby, drab, and devious. But I confess to a slight preference for Astata, which is a rugged individualist if nothing else.

The first male Bicyrtes ventralis make their appearance about the first of July, in time to enjoy the blossoms of white sweet clover. Most of the time they cruise over bare, sandy places a couple of inches above the ground, back and forth, back and forth, all day long. This is the "sun dance" or premating flight common to so many digger wasps. One fine day a female will dig her way out of the soil, and she will scarcely have time to clean the soil from her legs and wings before

being besieged by suitors. With one of them she will fly off
and settle on a poplar leaf long enough to be fertilized. This
act will be the fulfillment of being for the male, but for the
female it will serve as the prelude to an exciting life of bug-
hunting.

Bicyrtes ventralis normally nests in rather coarse, earthy or
gravelly sand. The female is a marvelous digger. Tilting her
head downward and her abdomen upward, she strikes the sand
with the long spines on her two front legs and causes the
sand to spurt out behind in a jet. Then she pauses, allowing
her body to assume a more horizontal position, then tilts
again and moves forward slightly. In this manner an oblique
burrow is drilled into the soil, with the sand falling well away
from the hole so that it never forms a definite mound as it
does in the burrows of many digger wasps. After a few minutes, the burrow is deep enough so that the soil has to be
cleared from it in two or more steps, the wasp having to back
up in the burrow to scrape the soil to the entrance, then stand
in the entrance and scatter it. After the burrow is about four

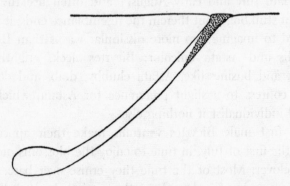

FIGURE 7. Profile of the nest of Bicyrtes ventralis.

inches long the female expands its end into a small cell, which
is only two or three inches vertically beneath the surface.
Bicyrtes then comes out, scrapes some soil into the entrance

[1] The spider wasp Dipogon sayi nests in holes in wood and commonly accepts "trap nests" such as these. This wasp has just left a ball of humus in the nest, to serve as part of a partition between cells, and has paused to clean her front legs. Wasps pause frequently in their activities in order to clean themselves. The legs are cleaned by passing them through the mouthparts, and various brushes on the legs serve to clean the antennae, the wings, and the body.

[2] Psammaecius nebulosus carrying a treehopper to her nest beneath an overhanging leaf on the ground. The treehopper is being held upside-down with the middle legs, a manner of prey carriage characteristic of Psammaecius and her relatives. Although treehoppers such as this one are "protectively colored," resembling spines or swellings on stems, they do not deceive these wasps, which, in fact, capture nothing else.

[3] The Nysson has done her dirty work. While the Psammaecius was away, she entered the nest and laid her egg beneath the thoracic shield of one of the bottom treehoppers, well hidden from sight. (Here the treehopper has been pulled apart to show the small egg glued to the underside of the shield.) Psammaecius finished provisioning the cell and laid her egg on the top treehopper, but the Nysson larva will hatch first and destroy the Psammaecius egg before commencing to eat up the treehoppers.

[4] Two very different wasps—in behavior as well as color and structure —are Astata unicolor (above) and Bicyrtes ventralis (below). Yet both subsist (as larvae) on immature stinkbugs, and in any one area often use the same species of bugs. The Astata has landed on the rough, hard soil of the garden, holding the stinkbug by the beak with her mandibles. Bicyrtes is seen entering her nest in a sandpit; she is able to scrape open the nest entrance with her front legs because the stink-bug is far back beneath her body, being grasped around the body with the wasp's middle legs. Since Astata is unable to do this, she leaves her nest open though it is often hidden by overhanging plants.

[5] A Great Golden Digger lands at the threshold of her nest in cinder fill beneath a lawn. Beneath her is slung a cone-headed meadow grasshopper. Large as the grasshopper is, she has carried it some distance in flight. Two or three of these large hoppers suffice to provision a cell. The wasp will eventually prepare several cells at the bottom of this gaping burrow.

[6] An Ammophila sleeps on a sweet clover seed stalk. Although the social wasps and some of the more advanced solitary wasps spend the night in their nests, the vast majority of wasps spend their inactive periods resting in vegetation. Each kind of wasp tends to have its own preferred sleeping place and its own way of grasping the plant. The species of Ammophila sleep gregariously, many of them on a single plant, though not in dense clusters. This particular pose is characteristic of Ammophila: the body forms a 45° angle with the plant and the wasp holds on with her mandibles and all three pairs of legs.

[7] A thread-waisted wasp, Ammophila urnaria, walks over the ground carrying a cater-pillar. The method of prey carriage in Ammophila is distinctive: the wasp seizes the caterpillar just behind the legs with its mandibles and also grasps it farther back with its front legs. This caterpillar is of about average size for urnaria, but some species of Ammophila use much larger ones, sometimes weighing as much as ten times the wasp's weight. Yet the wasp is able to carry them to the nest over various irregularities in the ground, while navigating correctly by means of landmarks she has memorized.

[8] A male Bembix spinolae pauses for refreshment on a goldenrod. The long beak is thrust into the blossom and the nectar sucked up—much like drinking through a straw. This wasp grew up, as a larva, on a diet of flies, and its progeny will be reared on flies. But most adult wasps feed upon nectar. The beak of Bembix is unusually long for a wasp; most wasps can feed only at blossoms with shallow nectaries.

[9] A larva of Bembix pruinosa moves along the line of flies provided for it by its mother. Behind it are the wings and hollowed-out bodies of flies that have been consumed. This larva is about four days old and is about two-thirds grown. In two or three days it will reach the end of the supply of flies and spin its cocoon in the end of the cell.

[10] A nearly mature larva of Bembix pruinosa approaches the end of her supply of flies. Behind the larva, the mother has thrown up a barrier of sand, closing off the end of the cell, into which the bits and pieces of flies which have been consumed have been swept. The practice of clearing the cell of debris occurs in only a few solitary wasps, and this manner of cell-cleaning is found, so far as is known, only in Bembix pruinosa.

[11] A female Bembix pruinosa plunges into her nest with a large horsefly. The wasp has opened the nest entrance with her front legs, only the base of which can be seen here. The hind legs are thrust out to the side for support, while the middle legs hold on to the sides of the fly. A moment after this, the wasp releases her grip with the middle legs and grasps the front of the fly with the tips of her hind legs, so that the fly is drawn behind her down the narrow burrow. This characteristic manner of prey carriage occurs in all species of Bembix and in many related wasps.

to close it, and makes an orientation flight. This appears to an observer to be a rather casual affair, but actually it serves to impress on the wasp many of the details of the environs of the nest, and without this impression she would never find her way back. She flies up obliquely backwards, hovers, moves from side to side, then returns again to scrape a little more sand in the entrance. This is repeated a few times with variations, and the wasp then makes a few loops over the entrance and is off.

But before long she flies in about eight to twelve inches high and descends to the well-covered nest entrance with her first stinkbug, which is clutched beneath her body tightly. She holds the bug upside down by her middle legs, and when she lands she scrapes open the entrance with her front legs while standing on her hind legs. Into the burrow she plunges, and is gone a minute or two. Coming out, she once again closes the entrance and often makes another, briefer orientation flight.

If one were to dig out the nest at this point he would find the stinkbug lying paralyzed on its back, head-in, at the bottom of the cell. On top of the stinkbug he would find the egg of the wasp, with its broader end attached between the leg-bases and its narrower end extending free and obliquely forward. If left alone the wasp will continue bringing in stinkbugs until the cell is full. Each one is placed on its back, head-in, like the first one. It takes about six to ten stinkbugs to fill the cell. Often it takes her the better part of a day to fill the cell, and if the weather changes for the worse she may not be able to fill the cell at all that day. I once found a nest which the female was still provisioning which contained a day-old larva. The egg had been laid late in the day August 11; on the next day the wasp for some reason brought in only a couple of bugs, and on the thirteenth it rained all day. When I dug out the nest on the afternoon of the fourteenth the larva was already working on the first bug even though the cell was still not full. But this is unusual; usually the female fills up the cell the same day the nest is dug.

Bicyrtes ventralis preys on many different kinds of stink-bugs, and often a single nest may contain two or more kinds. Invariably immature bugs are used. Doubtless these are a good deal more juicy and tender than the fully grown, winged adults. Now and then one finds squash bugs in a nest. These are not true stinkbugs, but they are closely related and have very similar stink glands. If we could train our Bicyrtes to specialize on squash bugs, perhaps growing squashes would not be such a headache!

When the cell is full, Bicyrtes begins to bite and scrape sand from the walls of the burrow and pack it in place. She packs it by curving the end of her body down and moving it up and down in such a way that the top of the last body segment (just above the sting) serves as a hammer. When the burrow is nearly full, she scrapes sand from the outside into it and pounds this down in the same way. When she has finished, it is as if nothing had ever disturbed the soil, while down in the sanctity of the cell the larva consumes its meal and, in a week or ten days, spins its cocoon.

Although ventralis is the only Bicyrtes which is common on Wasp Farm, another species, quadrifasciata, occurs in places not far away where there is more open sand of finer texture than ours. Sometimes the two species occur together, but when they do quadrifasciata is usually to be found nesting in the central part of open, fine-grained sandy areas, while ventralis is more apt to nest around the periphery. Quadri-fasciata also preys upon immature stinkbugs and now and then members of the squash bug family, but, being a slightly larger wasp, usually takes larger bugs. Although the two species are very much alike in almost every respect, there is one spectacular difference between them. In her orientation flight, quadrifasciata rises way up into the air several times and takes most of her loops and turns three or four feet high. When she returns with a bug, she comes in at an altitude of three or four feet and then, when properly poised, descends slowly, obliquely, directly down to the nest entrance. What particular advantage there may be in this high flight and slow descent to the nest is hard to say. At least it is in striking contrast to her more unassuming neighbor, ventralis, who glides in quickly only a foot or so above ground.

There is something appealing about Bicyrtes. They are elegant wasps, with bright bands on the abdomen and with glittering iridescent wings, and their direct and efficient mannerisms seem in keeping with their appearance. Astata is a horse of another color: black, as a matter of fact, and with a streak of mystery in its character. The most striking thing about Astata is the enormous eyes, which in the male seem to take up most of the head. The males can often be seen in July perching on heads of Queen Anne's lace, from which they now and then take flights so swift that they cannot be followed with the eye. The females appear a bit later, and for a long while I had no idea where they nested. Then one summer I discovered that they nested right under my nose, but in such a way that it was by sheer luck that I discovered them.

I happened to be out pulling carrots in the garden one day when a female Astata unicolor suddenly plopped onto the ground beside me carrying a big stinkbug. I could hardly believe she had a nest in the hard, stony clay of our garden, and supposed she must be pausing en route to some more suitable place. I stood back a few feet and watched, but the wasp seemed to be idling. She walked about, straddling her bug, and took short flights, landing now on the ground, now on the foliage of the carrots. After circling about for fully ten minutes, she suddenly walked under some drooping carrot leaves and disappeared. I moved the leaves and discovered a round, vertical hole in the ground which I would have taken for that of an earthworm. After a while Astata emerged from the hole without her bug and began walking and taking short flights in the same circuitous manner before finally taking off. Not only was the hole thoroughly concealed from above and decidedly unwasplike, but the wasp herself seemed determined that no one should catch her going in and out of such a place!

For the next couple of weeks I kept my eye on this wasp —as much as she would let me—and also discovered several other nests along the same row of carrots. But information came slowly. Often the wasps spent incredibly long periods away from the nest, or at other times they would go inside and not reappear for hours. They never "did" anything at the nest entrance, like other digger wasps. While they were out hunting the hole was left open, and at night or during showers it was closed by a plug of earth from within. At least I was able to determine exactly how the wasps carried their stink-bugs, and this proved to be very different from Bicyrtes. The wasp always grasped the base of the bug's antennae in her mandibles and straddled it, the bug being upside-down. In flight she held the bug close to her body with all three pairs of legs, but as soon as she landed she stood or walked about on all her legs and held the bug only with her mandibles. I also learned that individual wasps remain with the same nest for a week or more—perhaps their whole lives—rather than making a whole series of nests like Bicyrtes.

After a few days I decided it was time to dig out some of the nests I had marked to see what had been going on inside them. I did this with some trepidation, as the nests clearly would not be easy to dig out in this hard soil, and obviously each must contain several cells. I decided first to study what was known about Astata nests. After reading several articles I decided that I could expect almost anything. Clearly Astata did not lay her egg on the first stinkbug she brought in in the manner of Bicyrtes, yet the egg was always found on the bottom stinkbug in the cell. How she managed to lay her egg on the bottom of a stack of closely packed stinkbugs was confusing to several workers. So, while I didn't learn much that was useful from publications on the subject, I did sharpen my sense of adventure.

After digging a couple of active nests, it became clear that Astata did not take her bugs directly to a cell at all. Rather, she let them accumulate in the burrow only a few inches down, more or less covered with loose earth. Only after several had accumulated did she make a cell for them, put one in the bottom of the cell, lay an egg on it, then pack the cell tightly with as many more as it would hold (actually only two or three, as the bugs are quite large). The bugs are placed in the cell right side up, rather than upside-down as in Bicyrtes. The egg is laid on the underside in somewhat the manner of Bicyrtes, but it slopes backward instead of forward. One would think that the egg, being beneath the bottom bug, would be pushed against the ground. However, the cells of Astata are remarkably smooth-walled and are oval and sloping in such a way that there is a small space beneath the bottom bug, sufficient to accommodate the egg and the newly hatched larva. The larva, incidentally, feeds in an inverted position and has a hump on its back which assists it in pushing itself about in the cell.

I found from nine to fourteen cells in advanced nests of Astata unicolor. The cells were often very close together and sometimes formed a series along a single branch of the burrow. The wasp first digs a burrow not more than six to eight inches deep, then gradually shortens it as she builds successive cells. Thus the deepest cells in a nest contain more mature larvae or even cocoons while the uppermost cells have smaller larvae or eggs. The practice of making a close cluster of cells, many of them in series in the same branch of the burrow,

allows Astata to get by with very much less digging than
Bicyrtes, which digs a separate burrow for each cell. If this
were not so, Astata might soon wear herself out boring
through this hard soil.

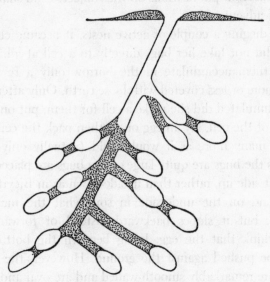

FIGURE 8. Nest profile of Astata unicolor.

Astata unicolor has nested in our garden each year, and we
have come to look forward to it much as we look forward to
our first catbird. I have had many chances to confirm my
original observations on the species, and have also become
familiar with the pre-mating flights of the males, which are
very different from those of Bicyrtes. Each male selects a stone
or clod of earth as a "favorite perch." For hours, even for days,
he may occupy the same perch, walking about a bit or sitting
motionless with his antennae extended rigidly. From time to
time he flies up swiftly, makes a loop, and comes back to his
perch. I have never seen them "do anything" during these
flights. Males from neighboring perches do not seem to fight

in defense of their territory, although a European worker (who was of course watching a different species of Astata) claims that if one male approaches the perch of another male too closely, the two roll together *"dans un corps-à-corps formidable."* Presumably the male meets a female on one of these flights, though in our garden the males seem to station themselves several yards away from the main nesting area of the females.

The old question of "nature or nurture" is easily answered with these wasps. The larvae of both Bicyrtes and Astata develop in the ground on a diet of paralyzed stinkbugs and, of course, have no contact with their mothers. Yet when they dig their way out of the soil they are as different as any two wasps can be—the males in their pre-mating flights, the females in the type of nests they dig, the way they handle their bugs, lay their eggs, and so forth. In fact, they are alike in hardly anything but their seemingly perverted hankering for stinkbugs!

Around our place Astata unicolor and Bicyrtes ventralis often use the same kinds of stinkbugs, and in other areas there are additional species of both groups, all hunting stinkbugs. Stinkbugs are common enough things, and most wasps I have observed seem to return like clockwork with their bugs. But it is true that they do nest in different types of soil: Bicyrtes ventralis in decidedly more sandy soil than Astata unicolor, and Bicyrtes quadrifasciata in still lighter, fine-grained sand. I have found the same thing to be true in other areas, where additional species were involved: they appear to compete for prey, but they nest in soils of different types and handle their prey in different ways.

On the other hand, one time when I was spending some time at the Archbold Biological Station, near Lake Placid, Florida, I found Bicyrtes quadrifasciata nesting side by side with a related wasp, Stictiella serrata. These wasps were remarkably similar in their nesting behavior; they each made unicellular nests in soft sand, they put their egg on the bottom prey in much the same manner, and they then filled up the cell with prey and closed the nest. But the hitch is this: though closely related to Bicyrtes, Stictiella preys not on stinkbugs but upon moths and butterflies! So, while these two behave much alike and appear to compete for nesting sites (though soft sand is plentiful enough in Florida), they certainly don't compete for their prey. These are very nice examples of a well-known axiom of biology, sometimes called Gause's hypothesis or the CCCC principle ("complete competitors cannot coexist"). The theory behind this principle is that if two species do in fact do everything alike—live in the same place, feed on the same food, and so forth—one of them is bound to do something very slightly better than the other and will, over a period of time, completely eliminate the other. But if in fact they impinge on their environment just a little differently in some respect, they can co-exist indefinitely. This can be demonstrated both mathematically and by laboratory experiments, though not, it should be confessed, to the complete satisfaction of everyone. I feel myself that there may be situations where this principle does not apply. But most digger wasps, and certainly Bicyrtes, Stictiella, and Astata, seem to illustrate the hypothesis very nicely.

CAST OF CHARACTERS

Bicyrtes ventralis: By-sir'-teez (Latin *bis*, two, plus Greek *kyrtos*, humped; a reference to two projections from the middle part of the body) ven-trail'-iss (Latin, of the belly).

Bicyrtes quadrifasciata: cwa-dree-fas-ee-ate'-a (Latin *quadri*, four, plus *fasciatus*, banded, with reference to the color pattern on the abdomen).

Astata unicolor: Ass-tate'-uh (Greek *astatos*, restless) you'-nee-cull-or (Latin, of one color).

Stictiella serrata: Stick-tee-el'-uh (Greek *stiktos*, spotted, plus *ella*, a Latin suffix meaning small) ser-rate'-uh (Latin, with saw teeth, a reference to a series of teeth on the middle legs of the male).

FOR FURTHER READING

Evans, H. E. "Ethological Studies on Digger Wasps of the Genus Astata (Hymenoptera, Sphecidae)." *Journal of the New York Entomological Society*, Vol. 65, pp. 159–85 (1957).

Krombein, K. V. "Some Notes on the Wasps of Kill Devil Hills, North Carolina, 1954" *Proceedings of the Entomological Society of Washington*, Vol. 57, pp. 145–60 (1955).

Parker, J. B. "A Revision of the Bembicine Wasps of America North of Mexico." *Proceedings of the United States National Museum*, Vol. 52, pp. 1–155 (1917).

CHAPTER FIVE

Great Wasps and Grand Vistas

The Greeks had a word for wasp: transliterated into our alphabet, the word was Sphex. Happily, the word Sphex has come down to us as the generic name of a group of handsome and spectacular digger wasps—a group that includes John Bartram's "Great Black Wasp from Pennsylvania," the elegant Great Golden Digger, and two wasps dear to the heart of the French naturalist Jean Henri Fabre—the yellow-winged Sphex and the Languedocian Sphex. In the insect world, most of the inhabitants of which are to us rather stealthy pygmies, Sphex is a bold and colorful giant. I know of few things more exciting than sitting beside a flourishing colony of these wasps and watching the females soar in, each with a katydid clutched beneath her: crisp, green songsters, creatures of sunshine and warm moonlit evenings, doomed to be devoured by flabby grubs in dark chambers. Here is a pretty example of immortality in the biological sense—the perpetuation of protoplasm: two or three green katydids consumed by a white grub and a few months later producing a black, orange, and gold digger wasp. Here is reincarnation in a very real sense!

It has been a source of disappointment that Great Golden Diggers (Sphex ichneumoneus) have never nested on Wasp

Farm. Some of our neighbors have been more fortunate. One back yard less than a mile away is blessed with a vigorous colony of them, and the owners of the yard enjoy the wasps and have no fear of them. For many years there was a colony of these wasps along a well-traveled path on the campus of Cornell University. So abundant and spectacular were they that they became something of a tradition among the summer school students. But gradually the colony declined, and now a bulldozer—that ubiquitous symbol of human progress—has completely transformed the area. One student, who was actually doing graduate work on a very different problem, became so absorbed with the wasps that he published a short account of the colony. The most detailed studies of the Great Golden Digger were made on another college campus about fifteen years earlier. The college was Woodstock College, Woodstock, Maryland, the student the Reverend John A. Frisch. I don't think college campuses have any particular attraction to digger wasps, but they do have a definite attraction for people likely to notice and study them!

A closely related (though very differently colored) digger wasp, the Great Black Wasp (Sphex pennsylvanicus) holds the distinction of being one of the first digger wasps—and certainly the first American digger wasp—ever to be the subject of a scientific paper. Its author was John Bartram, that untutored but marvelously gifted early American naturalist, the date 1749. Bartram was a Pennsylvania Quaker who corresponded with a fellow Quaker in England, Peter Collinson; later in his life he corresponded with and supplied specimens for many of the leading scientists of his day, including Linnaeus and Frederick the Great. It was Collinson who conveyed Bartram's observations on the Great Black Wasp to the Royal Society in London. Bartram's account expresses surprise that the wasps capture grasshoppers, and do not feed on fruits "as other wasps do." Bartram was aware that the hoppers were paralyzed by the sting and not actually killed; he was aware that about three hoppers are provided per cell, the egg being laid on the first one. The burrow is reported to be nearly an inch in diameter and over a foot long. Bartram's article is brief, but it is impossible to discover—more than two centuries later—any real misstatements of fact.

Several persons have studied the Great Black Wasp more recently and added many details to our knowledge. The wasps take several kinds of katydids and green meadow grasshoppers. They are indefatigable huntresses. Father Frisch plugged three nest entrances and found that five days later 252 katydids had been brought in and dropped on the ground by the wasps—an average of 16.8 per wasp per day—"a monument," he says, "to the wasp's stupidity as well as to her prowess as a huntress." They always fly to the nest with the prey, holding the base of the hopper's long antennae in their mandibles; they also embrace the hopper with their legs when they are flying, but hold them only by the antennae when they land. The nest entrance is left open, and when the wasps come in they leave the hopper on the threshold, enter the nest, then come out and grasp the hopper's antennae and draw it in. Eventually several cells are constructed per nest, all radiating out from a common chamber and all at about the same depth. The egg is laid with one end pressed against one of the front leg-bases, and the larva begins to feed through the membrane around the articulation of the leg. The hoppers remain alive, though immobile, for from one to two weeks, more than enough time for the wasp larva to complete its development.

Such are the bare essentials of the nesting behavior of the Great Black Wasp and the Great Golden Digger—for the two are much like in all important respects. But this bare outline conveys little of the excitement one feels on watching these creatures at work. The grasshoppers are often larger and heavier than the wasps, yet they are carried considerable dis-

tances in flight. Father Frisch reports that Great Golden
Diggers will often climb a shrub or weed and take flight
from there. As he says, "the wings move so rapidly they produce a sonorous hum, like the drone of an airplane motor,
which can be heard while the wasp is till some distance from
the nest." "It was evidently difficult," he says in another
place, "for the wasp to alter the course of her flight on short
notice. Repeatedly, burdened wasps crashed into me when
I was on the line of flight to their burrow." The wasps land
in front of their nests with a considerable "plop," then leave
the hopper on the threshold while they make an "inspection"
of the nest before drawing in the hopper. This particular
trait makes these highly photogenic wasps particularly easy
to work with. If one fails to snap the shutter quickly enough,
before the wasp releases the hopper and plunges into the nest,
he need merely turn the hopper around or move it away
from the nest. The wasp will then come out of the nest and
replace the hopper on the threshold, its head toward the hole,
then repeat the inspection of the nest—in the meantime afford-
ing the photographer another shot. This can often be repeated
again and again. Would that all wasps were as obliging to
a photographer!

Fabre's experiments along these lines are well known to
students of natural history, for Fabre's classic *Souvenirs Entomologiques* have been rendered into English and several
other languages. Fabre worked with the European Yellow-
winged Sphex (Sphex flavipennis), a species which differs
in no important respects from the Great Golden Digger and
the Great Black Wasp.

"Here are the particulars," says Fabre in the standard
English translation by de Mattos. "At the moment when the
Sphex is making her domiciliary visit, I take the [grasshopper]
left at the entrance to the dwelling and place her a few inches
farther away. The Sphex comes up, utters her usual cry,

looks here and there in astonishment and, seeing the game too far off, comes out of her hole to seize it and bring it back to its right place. Having done this, she goes down again, but alone. I play the same trick upon her; and the Sphex has the same disappointment on her arrival at the entrance. The victim is once more dragged back to the edge of the hole, but the wasp always goes down alone; and this goes on as long as my patience is not exhausted. Time after time, forty times over, did I repeat the same experiment on the same wasp; her persistency vanquished mine and her tactics never varied."

Fabre's experiments have been repeated a number of times on various species of Sphex. Indeed, his record of forty times has challenged biologists much as sixty home runs long challenged ballplayers. But Father Frisch established a new record which seems likely to hold for all time. As told in Reinhard's *The Witchery of Wasps*, he caused a Great Golden Digger to repeat her performance 103 times! Working in 95° heat, Father Frisch finally gave up and left the grasshopper in place; the wasp, "in absolute conformity to her traditions," then pulled the hopper into the nest. "So far as the wasp is concerned," he concludes, "we might still be at it."

But out of fairness to Sphex, it should be stated that everyone who has worked with these wasps has found much variation in their ability to adjust to such manipulations of their prey. Even Fabre, a great exponent of the "fixity of instinct," found a colony in which all the wasps, after being fooled a few times, simply grasped their hoppers and proceeded directly into their holes. His conclusion? "Craft is handed down . . . With Sphex as with us, the intellect differs with the province." But Father Frisch found that other wasps in the same colony as his record-breaker would adjust quickly and carry their hoppers directly into their nests.

Fabre, in his chapter "The Ignorance of Instinct," describes several additional experiments with Sphex. For example, he once found a Sphex closing up her fully provisioned nest. He interrupted the wasp, removed the fill from the burrow, and then removed the contents of the cell. The wasp, which was "on the watch" during these proceedings, then entered the nest, remained inside for some moments, then resumed her filling of the nest—even though she surely perceived that the cell was empty.

In the works of Fabre and many other students of wasps one finds accounts of other experiments of this general type. Reading them, one is much impressed by the lack of any consistent pattern in the results. Individual wasps differ; colonies differ; species differ; and most of all, people differ in their approach and interpretation. I believe Reinhard hit the nail on the head. "Until more is known about insect physiology," he says in his book, "and until all experiments are placed on a strictly scientific and mathematical basis, our inferences regarding insect psychology are bound to be shaky and uncertain." He notes that in the prey-manipulation experiments with Sphex, no one has attempted to control the distance to which the prey is removed, and this may well be all-important. One thinks of other factors, too, which have not been considered: age of the wasp, intensity of motivation as determined by the development of eggs in the ovaries and other more subtle factors, and so forth. What do such experiments mean anyway? Obviously the wasps perform satisfactorily under normal conditions, or they would soon become extinct. Obviously they are capable of learning in certain situations: indeed, their marvelous memory for details of the landscape is something to behold. Is it so remarkable that they fail to adjust to abnormal situations of various types? The normal life span of an adult female wasp may be something like a month. Is it not enough that their lives wind out successfully along the patterns they have inherited? I am fairly sure that most wasps do improve their performance somewhat from experience, but it is too much to ask them to cope with situations which they simply never encounter in nature.

These are some of the reasons why I almost never experiment with wasps, much to the disdain of some of my experimentally minded colleagues. It is not because I have no use for the experimental method; it is simply because one can waste a lot of time and print on experiments which are inappropriate or premature. In Chapter Three I described some very simple experiments which took very little time and told me a great deal. In later chapters I shall mention some of the experiments of Tinbergen and others on homing in digger wasps as well as Cooper's discoveries of how twig-dwelling species "know which way is out." These experiments were designed to bring out the significance of certain aspects of the normal behavior of wasps, and as such they have been more than worthwhile.

Say what you will, the urgent need is to know precisely what wasps and other creatures do under natural conditions. For a long while, until our understanding of animal behavior is on a very much higher plane than it is now, the important thing will be observation—by which I mean not casual glimpses of one or two individuals, but carefully drawn accounts of the behavior of many individuals in many different places. Since an understanding of variation in behavior of a given species in different environments and geographic areas is vitally important, even most of our common wasps provide good research material. But to provide a real contribution to science, such observations must be precise and quantitative. What species of katydids does the Great Golden Digger employ in your area, and in what proportions? What is the mean and range of variation in nest depth and in number of cells per nest? How do different individuals differ quantitatively in their digging, closing, or provisioning activities? How does one individual differ from day to day as she grows older?

These and a host of other questions can be answered with little more equipment than a notebook, a good pair of eyes, and unlimited time and patience.

What is the use of such information? Only from an abundance of data can we fully describe the behavior of a species in such a way that we can make meaningful comparisons with other species. And out of comparisons of species arise generalizations essential to an understanding of the evolution of behavior patterns. For example, we have enough data on the Sphecini—the tribe to which Sphex belongs—so that we can generalize that (1) they all prey upon grasshoppers and related insects, (2) they grasp the grasshopper by the antennae, and (3) they pack the soil in the burrow by pounding it with their head (rather than the tip of the abdomen like most digger wasps). The last trait is shared with Ammophila, considered in the next chapter, from which (and from certain structural data) we assume that these wasps have evolved from a common ancestor. Members of the genus Sphex make multicellular nests, each cell stocked with several grasshoppers, and nest colonially, from which we conclude that Sphex is a relatively advanced genus of its tribe (many members of which are strictly solitary and make unicellular nests stocked with a single grasshopper). But we still can't put our fingers on any real differences between the behavior of the Great Golden Digger and that of the Great Black Wasp. How do these wasps manage to co-exist if they do everything the same (as they surely don't)? And doubtless there are many more generalizations to be drawn when we can delineate the behavior of these wasps with greater assurance.

Some day, if we don't pave the whole world with concrete too soon, we will have a far fuller picture of the behavior of species, genera, and major groups of all animals. By that time the laboratory scientists will be able to tell us a great deal about the chemistry and physics of behavior. In the meantime, there is plenty to do for those of us who love the out-of-doors and who want to spend our hours richly and profitably. I have never been one to climb mountains simply because they were there. But if I heard of a digger wasp that nested on the snowfields of Everest . . .

CAST OF CHARACTERS

Sphex ichneumoneus: sfecks (Greek *sphex*, wasp) ik-new-moan'-ee-us (Greek *ichneumon*, a tracker).

Sphex pennsylvanicus: pen-sil-van'-ik-us (pertaining to Pennsylvania, where this wasp was first discovered).

Sphex flavipennis: fla-vee-pen'-iss (Latin *flavus*, yellow, plus *penna*, wing).

FOR FURTHER READING

Fabre, J. H. *The Hunting Wasps* (translation by A. T. de Mattos of Volume I of *Souvenirs Entomologiques*, 1879). New York: Dodd, Mead & Company (1915).

Frisch, J. A. "The Life-history and Habits of the Digger-wasp Ammobia ichneumonea (Linn.)." *American Midland Naturalist*, Vol. 18, pp. 1043–62 (1937). "The Life-history and Habits of the Digger-wasp Ammobia pennsylvanica (Linn.)." *American Midland Naturalist*, Vol. 19, pp. 673–77 (1938).

Ristich, S. S. "A Study of the Prey, Enemies, and Habits of the Great Golden Digger Wasp Chlorion ichneumoneum (L.)." *Canadian Entomologist*, Vol. 85, pp. 374–86 (1953).

CHAPTER SIX

Ammophila: Wasp and Legend

Beyond much question the most famous American digger wasp is Ammophila urnaria, and the most famous American wasp-watcher George W. Peckham, who immortalized Ammophila in a few pages of a book which his wife and he published in 1898, *On the Instincts and Habits of Solitary Wasps.* Dr. Peckham, a Milwaukee schoolteacher, later superintendent of public instruction and still later director of the Milwaukee Public Library, was qualified to practice both law and medicine, but he preferred the richer though more impecunious life of an educator and naturalist. Elizabeth and he became authorities on spiders and were leaders in the Wisconsin Natural History Society, a very active group about the turn of the century. Many of their summers were spent at the residence of Dr. Charles A. Leuthstrom, whose sandy gardens teemed with digger wasps, and before long they were authorities on wasps, too. They were ardent disciples of the great French naturalist Fabre, but often took issue with his interpretations of wasp behavior, feeling that he overemphasized the "fixity of instinct." The Peckhams were always alert for variation in behavior. Their book is still fascinating reading, though much of the argument now seems to have little point.

Ammophila was a favorite with the Peckhams, and they devoted the first and longest chapter of their book to the common northeastern United States species Ammophila urnaria. They describe how the wasp digs her short burrow in the soil, carrying off the pellets of earth rather than letting them accumulate at the nest entrance. When the nest is complete, the wasp searches about for one or more pebbles or lumps of earth with which to close off the burrow. This may involve considerable time, and some of the objects may be "tried for size" and then rejected. (We have found species of Ammophila using such things as sand burrs, rabbit droppings, and a single acorn to close off the burrow.) Finally some soil is scraped over the top to conceal the nest. Then the wasp flies off to find a caterpillar with which to stock the nest. She may not return for a day or even several days, but will have little trouble finding the nest, even though it is quite invisible to a human observer.

The ability of Ammophila to find her nest after a lapse of time is almost unbelievable. I remember one day in early July when I had gone out to our garden to pick our last lot of peas. It had been raining steadily for two days, and finally the sun was out and a host of insects had slipped from their confinement. An Ammophila urnaria had gotten to the peas before me and was making off with a green looper or "inch worm." (We use insecticides in our garden only in desperation, feeling that the insects pay for their keep by providing us with dramas such as this one.) The Ammophila proceeded straight down between two rows of peas with her caterpillar slung beneath her. When she reached the end of the garden, about twenty feet away, she made a right angle and followed a plow furrow for another five feet. Then she ascended the far side of the furrow and entered a patch of weeds where, with scarcely any hesitation, she dropped her caterpillar and began to dig. After much buzzing and biting of the soil, hard-packed after two days of rain, she uncovered her nest and dragged the caterpillar inside. The nest already contained a caterpillar with a small larva feeding upon it. Although urnaria ordinarily completes the provisioning of her nest all at one time, this one had clearly been interrupted by the rain and had had to wait nearly thirty-six hours. Yet she never hesitated in proceeding some twenty-eight feet to her nest.

My observations brought to mind a paper by H. T. Fernald, before his death some years ago a professor of entomology at the University of Massachusetts and an authority on the classification of digger wasps. Fernald's paper was titled "Did This Wasp Reason?" It was about an individual of the Florida race of urnaria which dragged her prey, a green caterpillar, first to a sidewalk, then about eight feet along the sidewalk, and finally to the nest, which was a short distance off the edge of the walk. Fernald asked whether the wasp reasoned that by using the sidewalk she could reach her nest with much less effort than by dragging it over the sand.

My urnaria had not really saved any effort by following first a row of peas and then a plow furrow: in fact she might have had somewhat smoother going had she cut diagonally and avoided the furrow. I surmised that the wasp had merely memorized these particular prominent landmarks and followed them to her nest. Of course, my thinking was influenced by my having read a very fine research paper on orientation in Ammophila by the Dutch ethologist G. P. Baerends. Baerends found that each female has a certain "home territory" in which she memorizes landmarks so well that she can find her nest even when she is artificially displaced within her territory. But outside her known territory she is unable to home properly, and if the landmarks are moved about she is much confused. Odors apparently play no part in finding the nest; it is purely a matter of recognizing landmarks. Major landmarks such as paths, furrows, mounds, bushes, and so

forth are especially important. Fernald was humanizing his
wasp when he wondered about her "reasoning." But then,
humanizing other creatures is a common human pastime.

But we have forgotten the Peckhams. Like others who have
studied Ammophila, they were much impressed by the homing abilities of the wasps. But what interested them most
was the behavior of wasps which had finished provisioning
their nests and were making the final closure of the nest.
Here they noticed much variation: one wasp "wedged two or
three pellets into the top of the hole, kicked in a little dust
and smoothed the surface over, finishing it all within five
minutes"; another one "worked for an hour, first filling the
neck of the burrow with fine earth which was jammed down
with much energy . . . and next arranging the surface of the
ground with scrupulous care, and sweeping every particle
of dust to a distance." Variation of this sort interested the
Peckhams greatly, and they described several individuals in
some detail. Finally they described the nest-closing behavior
of one particular individual in what has become one of the
most widely quoted paragraphs in the literature on solitary
wasps:

"Just here must be told the story of one little wasp whose
individuality stands out in our minds more distinctly than
that of any of the others. We remember her as the most
fastidious and perfect little worker of the whole season, so
nice was she in her adaptation of means to ends, so busy
and contented in her labor of love, and so pretty in her pride
over her completed work. In filling up her nest she put her
head down into it and bit away the loose earth from the sides,
letting it fall to the bottom of the burrow, and then, after
a quantity had accumulated, jammed it down with her head.
Earth was then brought from the outside and pressed in,
and then more was bitten from the sides. When, at last, the
filling was level with the ground, she brought a quantity of

fine grains of dirt to the spot and picking up a small pebble in her mandibles, used it as a hammer in pounding them down with rapid strokes, thus making this spot as hard and firm as the surrounding surface. Before we could recover from our astonishment at this performance she had dropped her stone and was bringing more earth. We then threw ourselves down on the ground that not a motion might be lost, and in a moment we saw her pick up the pebble and again pound the earth into place with it, hammering now here and now there until all was level. Once more the whole process was repeated, and then the little creature, all unconscious of the commotion that she had aroused in our minds, unconscious, indeed, of our very existence and intent only on doing her work and doing it well, gave one final, comprehensive glance around and flew away.

"We are claiming a great deal for Ammophila when we say that she improvised a tool and made intelligent use of it . . ." Indeed they were. But their account and their interpretation of it created quite a splash in the biological world. Twenty years later, the French naturalist Bouvier, in his book *The Psychic Life of Insects*, stated that "to employ . . . a pebble which serves as a tool is no longer instinct; it is a reasoning act, of which we find very few examples among insects." A few years later the British naturalist Major R. W. G. Hingston wrote a book entitled *Instinct and Intelligence*, in which he judged the Peckhams' account "the best instance of intelligence yet recorded in any insect." And McDougall, in his *Outline of Psychology*, compared Ammophila urnaria to "the man or ape who first took a stone in his hand to crack a nut." In recent years, one hears less of Ammophila, but she did make the pages of Evelyn Cheesman's *Insects Indomitable* and Ross Hutchins' *Insects—Hunters and Trappers*," and even made the dust jacket of Willy Ley's *Salamanders and Other Wonders*!

Somehow in all this, Ammophila the wasp has faded from the picture and been replaced by Ammophila the legend. One is reminded of the medieval scholars who are said to have argued about the number of teeth on a horse, quoting various ancient authorities, but never bothering to count them for themselves. Has no one else studied nest closure in Ammophila? As a matter of fact many have, and many have failed to note the "use of a tool" in the manner described by the Peckhams. However, a perusal of the literatures reveals some fifteen persons who have observed this behavior, and in a number of different species. Were their observations perhaps colored by their reading of the Peckhams' account? Ammophilas manipulate clods of earth in several different ways, and it is easy to be mistaken about the exact nature and significance of particular movements. Some years ago I made a number of observations in the Midwest on two species of Ammophila: procera, a large, showy species, and harti, a slender, silvery haired species characteristic of sand dunes. I watched many individuals of both species and never saw one "use a tool." I developed a hearty skepticism not only of the Peckhams' interpretation of this behavior but of the accuracy of their observations.

But sometimes young fellows are too eager to doubt the authorities. I remember my day of reckoning very well. It was a blazing hot day and I was seated in the bottom of a draw in central Kansas (what is that song about mad dogs and Englishmen?). There was really nothing much doing and I was considering leaving. An Ammophila juncea had dug a nest there two hours earlier, but she might not return to it for a day or two. Besides, I had already studied juncea briefly and found nothing special about the species; one or two caterpillars were used per nest, and the burrow was closed off with lumps of earth in the conventional manner, with no "use of a tool." But just as my mind had about erased the image of Ammophila and replaced it with that of a Coca-Cola, along came the female juncea with her caterpillar. She quickly dropped the caterpillar on the edge of the burrow, removed the temporary closure, went in, came out head-first, grasped the front end of the caterpillar, and pulled it in behind her. In a few moments she came out, selected a large pellet of earth, and carried it in head-first to serve as a plug for the burrow. Then she added two more smaller pellets and scraped in quite a bit of soil from the surface. Then she picked up another small lump, but this time instead of releasing it she held it in her mandibles as she moved her head up and down. She had used a tool! The whole drama was quickly over and somehow hadn't been nearly as dramatic as I had supposed. Or was it the heat?

It was only six days later that I saw a very similar performance on the part of a different species of Ammophila: aberti. I was camped on the banks of the Cimarron River in western Kansas: a lonely place, haunted by the ghosts of pioneers and by a lot of very-much-alive digger wasps. I found only one aberti nesting here, but she proved to be an energetic creature, stocking her nest with no less than ten caterpillars! When making the final closure, she wandered twenty feet from her nest before finding a pebble that suited her needs; she flew back to the nest with this and used it to pound the fill in the burrow several times before discarding it. A few years later I found this same species nesting on the beach of Laguna Madre in southern Texas and here using bits of shells and plant material as "tools." Now it happens that aberti had been seen using a pebble for pounding even before the Peckhams made their classic observation on urnaria. These observations were made by Samuel Williston, a pioneer geologist and student of flies, in 1892. In 1932 Charles Hicks published a paper on this same species. He studied many individuals and noted very little variation in behavior: every wasp pounded with a hard object when closing the nest. Hicks also studied another species, xanthoptera, in some detail, and again found that every individual he watched "used a tool."

Here then are two species which, so far as anyone knows, always exhibit this supposedly unique behavior. The case of juncea and urnaria is different, for here one finds that most individuals do not behave in this way. But now and then one does. The urnaria which I mentioned earlier as nesting in my garden was a "tool-user" par excellence, but that is the only occasion upon which I have seen urnaria perform in this way. Still another case is provided by harti and several other species, which have never been observed to "use a tool," even though some of them have been studied in some detail.

So it is no longer possible to question the accuracy of the Peckhams' observations. But one can question their interpretation of them. If the one individual urnaria which they saw pounding with a pebble was exhibiting intelligence, what shall we say of aberti and xanthoptera, in which this behavior is present in every individual? Are these "intelligent species"? And what of harti; is this a "stupid" species? Now it happens that harti nests in open sand dunes, where the grains are all of much the same size and pebbles hard to come by. And would a pebble serve a useful purpose? Have you ever taken a bucket of dry, fine-grained sand and tried to pound it into a firm plug? It simply can't be done. But aberti and xan-thoptera nest in firm soil, where a firm plug to the nest is not only possible but perhaps a necessity, for a loose plug in firm soil might be conspicuous to parasites or might weather away. It is worth noting that urnaria and juncea nest in many types of situations: sometimes in loose soil, sometimes in soil that is rather firm. There seems to be at least a very rough correlation between soil type and "tool-using." Need we say that the wasps decide what to do in each case? I would rather surmise that these wasps are instinctively capable of pounding with a pebble but that this behavior is only elicited under certain conditions, probably having to do with soil type. I would rather not even use the word "tool," because the very use of the word seems to me to imply that the wasp perceives the end to be achieved.

I confess I have never gotten over my initial disappointment on seeing the legendary Ammophila perform. "Tool-using" turned out to be nothing very different from the norm. Most Ammophilas block off the burrow with a large object selected from the environment, then add other smaller objects, each of them arranged neatly with the mandibles. Some of them are pulverized by the usual up-and-down movements of the head (all members of the subfamily to which Ammophila belongs pack the fill with blows of the front of the head). Some of the pellets are removed from the burrow if they do not suit (in the same way that the pellets comprising the temporary closure were removed when the Ammophila first arrived with her caterpillar). If a wasp puts a hard object in place, then begins to remove it, and if she rapidly alternates these actions as she performs her usual up-and-down movements, she is in effect pounding with the object. Once an Ammophila, nesting in firm soil, achieved this particular combination of pre-existing movements, natural selection would surely favor those individuals able to perform the behavior most effectively—for it seems to me a safe assumption that a firm plug is important to a species nesting in firm soil. Certainly this behavior is interesting, for it demonstrates how a new combination of pre-existing instinctive actions can achieve a new and quite different function. Indeed, the behavior is much more significant seen in this light, for it shows Ammophila to be a wasp of unusual and novel behavioral characteristics—but still behaving as a wasp and not as a human being.

I don't mean to imply that the last word has been said on Ammophila. Far from it! How difficult it is to know what motivates an animal! For that matter, do we always understand our own motivations? I am confident that Ammophila will have more students, for it is a fine figure of a wasp ("wasp waisted" to the nth degree). It is easy to work with, for the females go about their activities with seeming unconcern of human observers. I don't know of anything more exciting than to see a large Ammophila running over the ground with a huge caterpillar slung beneath her and then to follow her to her nest and watch the proceedings. There are something like fifty species in North America, and not one has really been studied in great detail. Baerends has shown, in Holland, how amenable these insects are to experimental manipulations. His extensive studies on a European species, along with the briefer comparative studies which various people have made on other species, have already carried us a long way beyond the Peckhams. And if recent studies have tended to deflate Ammophila the legend, they have made Ammophila the wasp vibrantly alive with possibilities.

CAST OF CHARACTERS

Ammophila urnaria: Am-mof'-ill-uh (Greek *ammos*, sand, plus *philia*, love) earn-air'-ee-uh (Latin *urna*, a container for the ashes of the dead, perhaps an allusion to the nest cells).

Ammophila procera: pro'-sir-uh (Latin, long and slender).

Ammophila harti: hart'-eye (named after Professor C. A. Hart, a noted Illinois biologist).

Ammophila juncea: jun'-see-uh (Latin, rush-like).

Ammophila aberti: ab'-bert-eye (named after Abert).

Ammophila xanthoptera: zan-thop'-terr-uh (Greek *xanthos*, yellow, plus *pteron*, wing).

FOR FURTHER READING

Evans, H. E. "Observations on the Nesting Behavior of Digger Wasps of the Genus Ammophila." *American Midland Naturalist*, Vol. 62, pp. 449–73 (1959).

Peckham, G. W. and E. G. "On the Instinct and Habits of the Solitary Wasps." *Wisconsin Geological and Natural History Survey Bulletin* No. 2, 245 pp. (1898). (Republished in 1905, with some changes, as: *Wasps Social and Solitary*. Boston: Houghton Mifflin Company.)

CHAPTER SEVEN

The Secret Lives of Sand Wasps

There is scarcely a place on the face of the earth more sterile and uninviting than the central part of an active sand dune. The slightest wind picks up handfuls of sand particles and drives them along. The sun pours down torrents of heat and the bright surface hurls it harshly back. Any rain that falls percolates so rapidly through the sand that it leaves no impression at all. Temperatures often rise to 90–100° by day, and the sand surface commonly measures 125° or even more. Studies have shown that physical conditions in sand dunes are much the same the world over, whether it be in the Sahara or in Aweme, Manitoba. Even a plant sturdy enough to withstand the heat and dryness soon has the sand blown out from under its roots or piled in drifts over its branches. Little wonder that such places are so devoid of life!

But visit a sand dune—not in the cool of evening or of winter or spring, but in the hottest part of the day and in the hottest part of the year—and you may find it teeming with a particular insect which, in fact, occurs nowhere else. This is Bembix pruinosa, a stout-bodied wasp brightly patterned with pale yellowish-green markings. At the proper season, one rarely finds a sand dune east of the Rocky Mountains that lacks a thriving colony of these wasps. Along with the wasps often occur some of their parasites—certain types of flies and of hairy, wingless wasps known as "velvet ants." But that is very nearly all; the wasps and their parasites make up almost the entire diurnal fauna of the dunes.

Only a remarkable insect can thrive in this habitat. It must be able to adjust to or avoid the extremes of temperature and aridity, not only for itself but also for its more delicate eggs and larvae. It must be able to rear its progeny where they will not be exposed or buried deeply by blowing sand. It must be able, without fail, to find its nest in a vast expanse of shifting sand. And it must be able to survive in spite of numerous parasites. It so happens that most of the parasites of sand wasps are not host-specific: that is, they attack a variety of different wasps in different situations. Here Bembix pruinosa is at a distinct disadvantage: the parasites are wide-ranging and ever-present, but the wasps are restricted to suitable parts of active sand dunes. Ordinarily, when parasites cause the decline of a population, they bring about their own decline, too, since they create a shortage of suitable hosts. But not so here: if Bembix declines, the parasites continue to live on other hosts in surrounding areas, areas that Bembix is unable to invade. Only by "outwitting" its parasites can this species maintain its numbers.

By various and often unique behavioral devices, Bembix pruinosa is able to accomplish all these things. But before I describe some of these behavioral peculiarities, let me digress for a moment to say a bit about one of the more "ordinary" members of the same genus, Bembix spinolae. Like quite a number of species of Bembix, spinolae lives in less formidable situations and is not nearly so restricted to one particular ecological niche. I have found spinolae now and then on Wasp Farm, and it is not uncommon in various local sand pits. But to find pruinosa one has to drive some sixty miles to the nearest real sand dunes. Spinolae occurs here, too, but only around the periphery of the dunes proper.

The behavior of Bembix spinolae is relatively simple, yet in some ways a bit more complex than any of the wasps we have considered up to this point. The female spinolae digs an oblique burrow about six inches long, terminating in a small oval cell about four inches below the surface. When the burrow and cell are complete, she captures a fly, places it in the cell, and lays her egg upright against the side of the fly. No further flies are placed in the cell until the egg is nearly ready to hatch, about two days later. Then she brings in two

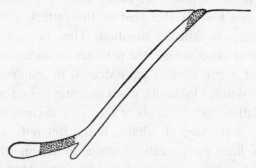

FIGURE 9. Nest profile of Bembix spinolae.

or three more flies, the next day several more, and so on; when the larva is quite large, after about five days of feeding, as many as twenty flies per day may be provided. When the female is not bringing in flies she spends most of her time inside the nest, right outside the cell. Since the flies usually die from the effects of the sting and hence do not remain in good condition for long, the mother compensates by employing "progressive provisioning," so that the larva has freshly killed flies at all times. The larva feeds only upon the soft parts of the flies, leaving a mass of wings and hollowed-out bodies, which eventually form a mat on the bottom of the cell. After about five days of provisioning, the female fills up the burrow and begins a new one nearby.

Bembix spinolae has many parasites. Some of them attack the larva directly—such as the bee flies, which drop their eggs into the nest entrance, and the velvet ants, which enter the cell and lay their eggs through the wall of the cocoon. Others live upon the bodies of the flies in the cell, forcing the mother wasp to bring in a great many additional flies and often causing the wasp larva, in spite of this increment, to die of starvation. This type of parasitism is exhibited by quite a number of small flies that deposit small, live-born maggots in the cell or on the body of the prey as it is brought into the nest. These larvae grow rapidly into ravenous maggots, as many as a dozen or more of which may inhabit a single cell.

Bembix spinolae seems to have few means of avoiding these parasites. The wasps do remove the telltale pile of sand at the entrance to the burrow, and they do keep the burrow closed at the entrance nearly all the time—mechanisms doubtless functioning to make the nest as inconspicuous as possible to parasites—but apparently the species thrives mainly because it is ecologically versatile. That is, if parasites become overly abundant, individuals radiate out into neighboring habitats and establish new colonies—something a species like pruinosa is unable to do.

The nesting behavior of pruinosa is much more elaborate than that of spinolae. As might be guessed, the nests are much deeper than they are in spinolae. The top layers of sand, in a dune, are dry and exceedingly hot; but a foot or two down, the sand is much cooler and more moist. Also, in a shallow nest the cell might soon be exposed to the deadly heat of the surface by the action of wind. In small, sheltered dunes, I have found the average depth of the cell to be only about eight inches. In larger dunes the depth of the cell varies from ten to twelve inches, and in one very large dune system along the banks of the Red River in Texas, I found the cells to be nearly two feet beneath the surface. Apparently, isolated colonies of the wasp become adapted to conditions in their area: the more blowing sand, the deeper the nests. It would be interesting to transplant wasps from a colony in a small, protected dune to a very large dune and study their survival.

Not only is pruinosa's nest deeper than spinolae's, it is considerably more complex. When the female is about to start a nest, she digs a bit in one spot, then backs up an inch or two, digs again, backs up again, and so on. The result is a series of little pits connected by a straight line. If the texture of the sand is suitable, she then digs down an inch or two and prepares a horizontal tunnel below the sand surface— and just beneath her line of little pits, which apparently function to insure that no serious cave-ins will occur here. This "preliminary burrow" may be as much as twenty inches long. After it is finished, the wasp returns to the entrance, levels off the pile of sand that has accumulated, then enters the burrow and closes it from the inside. She then goes to the far end of the preliminary burrow and begins to dig obliquely down into the sand, pushing the soil from this "true burrow" into the preliminary burrow, which is soon completely filled up. At the bottom of the true burrow, which may

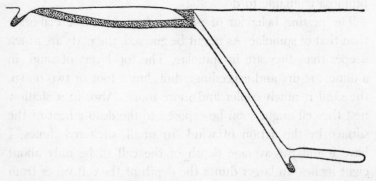

FIGURE 10. Profile of a completed nest of Bembix pruinosa.

be as long as or even longer than the preliminary burrow, the wasp constructs a cell—not a simple, oval cell as in spinolae, but a slender chamber averaging eight inches in length. Thus, the total length of the nest, including preliminary burrow, true burrow, and cell, may be as much as a yard and a half: dug by a wasp about half an inch long. Yet this nest is used for rearing only a single larva, and a new one is constructed for each successive offspring.

After finishing her nest, the female lays her egg at the far end of the cell and proceeds to wait inside the nest until the egg is nearly ready to hatch, a matter of about two days. Then she leaves the nest, going out this time not by way of the preliminary burrow, which has been filled with sand and abandoned, but directly up the true burrow and out to the surface. This involves preparing a new nest entrance, which is first cleared out by digging and then filled in briefly to make a temporary closure while the wasp goes off to catch a fly. Each day the larva receives a few more flies, but these are not merely packed into the cell as in spinolae; rather, they are lined up single file along the very long brood chamber. The larva moves down the chamber as it feeds, consuming one fly after another and leaving the remains behind. It is a temptation to say that the pruinosa larva is fed cafeteria-style!

If one examines a nest after the larva is three or four days old, he finds that the larva has moved the greater part of the length of the cell. A short row of fresh flies, recently added by the mother, still confronts it. Behind it ought to lie the loose wings and hollowed-out carcasses of flies that have been devoured: but where are they? Does this larva eat the entire fly? A little further study shows that the cell is considerably shorter than it ought to be, and some further digging reveals the fly remnants in a compacted mass at the end of the original cell, walled off by a barrier of sand. Apparently, the mother

wasp has raked all the debris into the end of the cell and then
thrown up a barrier of sand to seal it off from the larva and
the fresh flies. At about this time, the wasp closes up her
burrow finally and completely, leaving the larva to finish its
growth on the remaining flies and spin its cocoon. If, for some
reason, the final closure of the nest is delayed a day, the wasp
may prepare a second cache of fly remains and thereby shorten
the cell still further.

For a long while, I was at a loss to explain this odd behavior. What possible difference could it make whether or
not the larva lives in a clean cell or in a cell glutted with the
remains of consumed flies (as in spinolae and most other
species)? After digging out over eighty nests of pruinosa, I
remarked upon one fact: this species is apparently never attacked by the maggots which commonly infest the nests of
other species. Such maggots live in the fly debris, but also
compete with the larva for fresh flies. Perhaps pruinosa has
found a way of overcoming them—for as a result of its cell-
cleaning actions, any developing maggots might soon find
themselves segregated from the main part of the cell. It may
be that pruinosa long ago acquired the ability to sweep fly
bodies into the tip of the cell. Once this was achieved, natural
selection doubtless favored any elongation of the cell, so that
this sweeping behavior could be performed more effectively.
The remarkably long cell of Bembix pruinosa may have
evolved in such a way.

At least, this seems the most plausible hypothesis for the
strange nesting behavior of this wasp. It seems probable, too,
that the long, complex burrow has evolved as a means of
deterring parasitism by bee flies and velvet ants. The closures
of the nest, both temporary and permanent, are so thorough
that the nest entrance is at all times quite invisible to a human
observer, unless he sees the wasp entering or leaving. And
perhaps it is as confusing to a parasite as it long was to me,

to have the nest entrance shift as much as twenty inches between the start of the preliminary burrow and the beginning of provisioning!

Bembix pruinosa, and a few other species of its genus, lays its egg in the empty cell, before any flies have been brought in. In spinolae and most other species, the egg is laid on a fly, but since the fly is killed by the sting it tends to deteriorate somewhat by the time the egg hatches. Thus, in Bembix, this first fly has become a mere pedestal for the egg: it is usually not eaten by the larva, which feeds on the fresh flies supplied by the mother. By omitting this first fly, pruinosa is able to omit that first hunting trip: and also avoid the chance that a parasitic fly might deposit maggots on this first fly as it is brought into the nest, as happens with some other digger wasps.

Concealing the nest so thoroughly, and living as it does in broad areas of uninterrupted shifting sand, this wasp must have remarkable powers of orientation. I have often sat in the midst of a great colony of these wasps, watching females return again and again to nest entrances that were completely invisible to me. All the while, the breeze blows lightly, and swirls of sand continually change the contours of the sand dune. The nearest tree is several rods away and the nearest tufts of grass lie well outside the wasp colony. And yet the wasps go back and forth without error, finding their own nest among the hundreds of seemingly identical nests scattered over the dune. How do they do it? What landmarks can possibly be used? (There is no evidence that odor plays any role in nest-finding.) This is a subject we'll return to later, in chapter eleven. Obviously pruinosa has solved this problem, too, just as it has solved the problem of rearing its offspring under seemingly impossible physical conditions and in the face of seemingly inescapable attacks of wide-ranging parasites.

Most of the elaborate behavior patterns of pruinosa have a discernible function, though sometimes (as in the case of the very long brood chamber) some rather subtle hypotheses have to be invented to explain them. There are some other aspects of the behavior of this species which I confess I am quite unable to explain in functional terms. For example, the males of this species have a very special type of prenuptial flight, which I call the "hopping dance." The males take a series of short flying hops over the sand, like nothing so much as small toads, for no apparent reason. This hopping dance occurs in one other species of Bembix (also a sand dune species) but in no other digger wasps known to me. It has been suggested to me that the males hop simply because the sand surface is too hot for them to sit still—the proverbial cat on a hot tin roof. But the dance occurs with equal intensity and with greater frequency in the morning hours, before the sand surface is extremely hot; furthermore the females never indulge in such hopping. So far as I can see it is simply a special type of courtship behavior.

Another bit of strange behavior occurs after the female has completed provisioning her nest and filled up the burrow with sand. One would think it would suffice to scrape a little sand over the top of the filled burrow so that velvet ants could find no trace of it. But the female pruinosa spends a great deal of time at it, most of it going in straight lines away from the nest entrance up to a distance of six to twelve inches. She kicks sand as she goes, then comes back and makes another line in a slightly different direction. The result is a somewhat star-shaped pattern of lines on the sand, at first quite conspicuous, so that upon entering a dune for the first time one can often spot various just-filled nests by the pattern of radiating lines. Of course, wind action removes these lines in a matter of a few minutes to a day or two. What possible function they serve I have no idea.

Deducing the functional significance of various structures and behavior patterns is a fascinating game. Sometimes it is very easy: there is no question that the long spines on the front legs of Bembix serve for raking sand, or that the backward thrusts of the front legs and synchronized elevation of the abdomen result in the throwing backward of a jet of sand. At other times functions are less obvious but can be deduced, as in the case of the various closures of the nest, the long brood chamber of pruinosa, or—turning to a structure—the stronger teeth on the mandibles of species which nest in heavier soil (where the mandibles are employed for loosening the soil). But we are always left with a residue of apparently functionless or "non-adaptive" features, such as the "radiating lines" behavior of pruinosa mentioned above. Most species of Bembix have an unusual kink in one small vein of the front wing, though this kink is lacking on one species of Bembix and in all related wasps. Again, I cannot imagine the functional significance of this.

If our current ideas about evolution are correct, all features of living things should have some functional value. Natural selection continually acts to favor better adaptation to the environment and to remove non-adaptive features. Of course, it sometimes happens that a structure or behavior pattern serves an important function and then, as a result of other adaptive changes in the organism, ceases to serve a useful function. It will be reduced and probably eventually eliminated, but this takes time: the human appendix is a good example of such a "vestigial" feature. It is also possible that some features of no functional value are linked genetically to other very important characteristics, and in this way carried along indefinitely. But the usual explanation of "non-adaptive" characteristics I'm sure, is simply that we humans aren't yet able to detect the functional value of some things. At one time there were many things about the behavior of Bembix pruinosa that made no sense to me. Now I think I understand the adaptive significance of many of its behavior patterns, though I am probably wrong on some of them. Perhaps someday I will understand more.

CAST OF CHARACTERS

Bembix pruinosa: Bem'-bix (Greek, a buzzing insect) pru-in-oh'-suh (Latin, covered with frost or powder).

Bembix spinolae: spin-oh'-lee (named for the Italian entomologist Spinola).

FOR FURTHER READING

Evans, H. E. *Studies on the Comparative Ethology of Digger Wasps of the Genus Bembix*. Ithaca, N.Y.: Comstock Publishing Associates (1957).

CHAPTER EIGHT

The Saga of a Beachcomber

One of the most appealing things about insects is that they can be depended upon to behave pretty much according to their own set patterns. We humans open our evening papers with trepidation, not knowing what strange new channels human behavior may have entered upon today. What new satellites are orbiting? What is the strontium 90 level? But the crickets are singing the same old songs, the bean beetles eating beans in the same old way. And yonder cockroach doubtless waved his antennae about in the carboniferous forests much as he does among the tomes of my library.

Of course, there is a great deal we don't know about the behavior of insects. Stereotyped though it may be, it is the product of eons of evolution. After a little study one can often predict pretty much what an insect will do at a given point in its life cycle and under a given set of conditions, but it is not easy to explain why one kind of insect does it one way and another kind another way. Of explanations there are two types. One is that of the physiologist, consisting of analyses of the sensory apparatus, the nerve tracts, and the responses elicited. Another is that of the evolutionist, who compares related species and develops hypotheses regarding the development of specific behavior patterns in time and the environmental pressures which may have molded them. Both types of explanations are, of course, perfectly valid, but when both have had their say we are very often left with a multitude of uncertainties.

Few animals are more amenable to comparative studies of behavior than are the digger wasps. Digger wasps are fascinating things to watch, and one soon learns that each species and genus has its own "personality," that is, its own particular set of characteristic behavior patterns. Study a few and you will soon be concocting theories right and left—see, for example, most of the standard literature in the field. Indeed, the wistful hymenopterist, out in his garden watching wasps and spinning his philosophy, has become almost a stock figure in biology.

One of the features of digger wasps that has attracted much attention is their specificity for a certain type of prey. A species of Bembix, for example, can be depended upon to capture flies, while a Gorytes will take leafhoppers, a Bicyrtes stinkbugs, a Philanthus bees, and so on. All species of Trypoxylon prey upon spiders, but Trypoxylon clavatum can be expected to take crab spiders and jumping spiders, while Trypoxylon striatum preys largely upon orb-weavers. In a given area the digger wasps will exploit many sources of fresh arthropod food, but rarely will any two species compete seriously for the same food. This is in itself something of an explanation, for the evolution of behavior patterns which allow an animal to exploit a rich and untapped source of food is surely a formula for success. A more functional explanation might be that a given wasp either (a) inherits a tendency to hunt in a certain environmental situation and to respond only to a specific image, that is, that of a fly, leafhopper, or whatnot, or (b) "remembers" the odor of the food it ate as a larva and seeks out that odor when searching for food for its own larva. There are adherents of both these views (which are not, incidentally, mutually exclusive), but the critical experiments have yet to be performed.

But what are we to say of Microbembex monodonta, that most abundant of all digger wasps, inhabitant of almost every spit of open sand from Canada to South America? It has been known for a long time that Microbembex doesn't really "prey" on anything at all. The female picks up dead or disabled arthropods of all kinds and stuffs them into the nest as food for the larva. So far as I know, Microbembex is unique among digger wasps in being a scavenger, a beachcomber if you like, a collector of cripples and corpses. While the larvae of other digger wasps are consuming one delicate morsel or another, that of Microbembex is eating garbage and thriving. Rather than exhibiting any real hunting behavior, the female Microbembex cruises over the sand, swooping down now and then to pick up objects lying there. Some of these are rejected (for example, if they are of plant origin), but virtually all dead arthropods and pieces thereof, regardless of their size or state of preservation, are toted off to the nest.

Recently I reviewed some of my field notes and some of the published observations on Microbembex in order to get some idea of the types of "prey" used. As you read the list which follows, bear in mind that, for example, Aphilanthops frigidus preys only upon queen ants of the Formica fusca group. Microbembex monodonta has been found to utilize members of two classes of arthropods and no less than ten orders of insects. Here is the list.

Araneae (spiders). Used commonly; the spiders are usually immature running or jumping spiders, often mangled, incomplete, or desiccated.

Orthoptera (crickets and grasshoppers). A few records of immature crickets, one of a pygmy mole cricket, several for pieces of grasshoppers.

Corrodentia (book and bark lice). A single adult bark louse found in one nest.

Hemiptera (true bugs). Leafhoppers used very commonly, both nymphs and adults. Also recorded: jumping plant lice, tarnished plant bugs, milkweed bugs, and others.

Ephemerida (mayflies). Used extensively where Microbembex nests along the shores of lakes; presumably these are mayflies which flew the preceding evening and died on the sand or were washed up along the shore.

Trichoptera (caddisflies). I have only one record, though they may well be used commonly in some situations.

Neuroptera (ant lions, lacewings). Dried, shriveled ant lion larvae taken from nests on two occasions.

Lepidoptera (moths and butterflies). Small caterpillars of various kinds, often in poor condition, used fairly commonly. I have one record of a pupa and two of small adult moths.

Hymenoptera (sawflies, wasps, bees, ants). Ants sometimes used in numbers, especially workers; in one nest I found sixteen ants of four species. Dead digger wasps or pieces of them are sometimes used; I once saw a Microbembex carrying a large whole digger wasp (Priononyx) which was limp and apparently had been killed and sucked dry by a robber fly. Sawfly larvae and adult bees and parasitic Hymenoptera are also used occasionally.

Coleoptera (beetles). Used very commonly, both larvae and adults. Especially commonly used are ground beetles, wireworms, diving beetles, leaf beetles, and lady beetles, though many other kinds have been reported. On three different occasions I have taken larvae of tiger beetles from nests of Microbembex. These larvae live in holes in the sand and are vicious predators; presumably the Microbembex found them dead.

Diptera (flies). Midges and mosquitoes are commonly used,

especially in beach areas. Various larger flies, particularly blowflies, have been found in many nests.

This list could probably be lengthened considerably if one were to dig out great numbers of Microbembex nests and survey the contents. It could surely be lengthened experimentally by simply killing or disabling various arthropods and throwing them on the sand near colonies of the wasp. The females readily pick up such booty, and doubtless all orders of insects could eventually be added to the list in this way, perhaps even such things as centipedes, millipedes, ticks, and scorpions. One wonders if they will take sow bugs or dried aquatic Crustacea. How about annelid worms or bits of mollusks? Here is a wonderful and easy problem for someone idling away a summer at a beach resort!

There are many observations and a few simple experiments which indicate that Microbembex never takes fully active arthropods. Nevertheless, whatever sort of animal detritus the female picks up, she always seems to curve her abdomen forward and sting it. Whether any venom is actually injected we do not know. To see a Microbembex pick up a dried fragment of an insect or an empty puparium and appear to sting it is always a bit of a shock: in human terms, it is an incredibly stupid thing to do. Actually, what one is observing is perhaps an unusually good example of a vestigial instinctive act.

That Microbembex still stings the "prey" (or at least goes through the motions) suggests that its life as a scavenger may have developed rather recently in geologic time. There is much other evidence to support this view. Almost everything else about the structure and behavior of Microbembex is very much like that of the related genus Bembix, in fact like that of the more specialized members of that genus such as pruinosa, discussed in the preceding chapter. The elaborate behavior involved in making the final closure of the nest is

especially like that of pruinosa. It is also significant that
Microbembex lays its egg in the empty cell, before any provisions have been brought in. This behavior occurs in only
a few digger wasps, all of them among the more highly evolved
Bembicini. Microbembex, a small genus of small wasps, restricted to the Americas, must surely have evolved not too
long ago from some already well-advanced Bembix, perhaps
much like pruinosa.

It is also worth noting that the "prey" of Microbembex
is always carried to the nest by the middle legs, a trait
characteristic of Bembix and all members of this section of
the digger wasp family Sphecidae. Watching Microbembex,
one can't help feeling that it would be better off if it could
abandon this particular mode of transportation for something
better adapted to the diversity of its booty. The species of
Bembix clamp their middle legs neatly around the thorax of
the fly and hold it close beneath their abdomen. But in carrying on one trip a minute worker ant and on the next trip a
large chunk of a dried beetle, Microbembex seems hard put
to adjust her limited repertory of carriage movements to the
size and shape of the insect. One often sees a Microbembex
drop her insect, pick it up again, drop it again, and so forth.
If she were only free to use her mandibles and all her legs,
one feels, some of her problems might be solved!

Watching Microbembex is sometimes a frustrating experience. Both males and females appear to spend a great deal
of their time doing nothing of any importance: flying about
the sand, idling on flowers, digging unnecessary burrows, etc.
Near every colony of Microbembex there is always a bank of
sand riddled with a great many holes; in fact, one can often
spot Microbembex colonies by watching for these clusters
of open holes. The wasps do not nest in these holes, but in
a different area nearby. Perhaps they make these holes in

which to spend the night, then abandon them and dig a different one the next night. One could, of course, be rashly anthropomorphic and say simply that they just like to dig holes. Is it possible that Microbembex is a sufficiently "sophisticated" wasp that it indulges in play? One certainly obtains that impression after a few hours of watching them. However, I have sometimes seen the bee fly Exoprosopa, a major parasite of these wasps, dropping its eggs into these open, blind burrows (the real nests of Microbembex are always kept closed). Perhaps these "play" burrows really have a more subtle explanation.

There are indeed many things about Microbembex that tempt one to question and to theorize. Do they, in fact, play? Do they, in fact, actually sting the inert arthropods which they pick up? Can the adult wasp be said to "remember" what it fed on as a larva, when in fact it fed on all kinds of things in all states of decay and desiccation? Under what conditions might Microbembex have evolved from Bembix? Was there a long period of fly scarcity in some area such that natural selection favored smaller wasps nourished on carrion rather than on live flies?

But as yet the published reports on Microbembex consist of less than thirty pages, much of that superficial or repetitious. Here is a remarkable animal available wherever there is sand. Here is a way to get away from the vicissitudes of human behavior into a realm where all is certain—and in its own way excitingly uncertain.

CAST OF CHARACTERS

Microbembex monodonta: My′-crow-bem-bix (Greek *mikros*, small, plus *bembix*, a buzzing insect) mon-o-dont′-uh (Greek *monos*, single, plus *odontos*, tooth, a reference to the simple, one-toothed mandibles).

FOR FURTHER READING

Hartman, C. "Observations on the Habits of Some Solitary Wasps of Texas." *Bulletin of the University of Texas*, No. 65, pp. 1–72 (1905).

See also the reference to P. and N. Rau at the end of Chapter Two and the reference to J. B. Parker at the end of Chapter Four.

CHAPTER NINE

Build Thee More Stately Mansions

Nearly everyone is familiar with the delicate grass nest of the chipping sparrow and the rude mud cup of the robin. Some have watched the woodpecker hew its nest from wood, the kingfisher tunnel in a clay bank along its favorite stream, or the cliff swallow plaster its mud sphere to a rocky ledge. Justly famous are the birds for the infinite variety of their nests.

Yet the wasps use all these methods of nest construction and a number of others as well. Clay banks and bare, sandy places are frequently riddled with the nests of digger wasps. Some wasps bore in rotten wood or remove the pith from stems and nest in the cavity. The mud daubers fasten their adobe cells to hollow trees, bridges, and the roofs and walls of open buildings. Hornets and yellow jackets have mastered the art of making paper from wood pulp and using it to build elaborate apartment houses. But, alone among the wasps, the grass-carrier, Isodontia harrisi, uses grass as her principal building material.

Grass, of course, is the commonest ingredient of most birds' nests, and one often sees a bird flying to its nest with a straw in its bill. It is a far more remarkable sight to see Isodontia flying through the air with a straw several times

the length of her body! For a number of years I have seen
these wasps flying high into crevices in our house, perhaps
into holes made by carpenter bees. I have never studied these
nests, as that would require taking the house apart, but on
other occasions I have found their nests in the hollow twigs
of dead sumacs. Others have found them in quite a variety
of natural cavities, their nests always stuffed with grasses
and other plant materials. Actually, Isodontia is a true digger
wasp, not unrelated to the Great Golden Digger which we
met in Chapter Five. One wonders if, at some time in the
past, competition for nesting sites favored its adopting this
unusual nesting behavior.

It was A. S. Packard, in 1869, who first reported on the
nesting behavior of Isodontia. Packard, as a youth, used to
go to bed evenings with the windows open and the lights
burning, so that he could observe the many insects that flew
to the light. Later he became a professor of zoology at Brown
University and one of the pioneer entomologists in the country. In his classic *Guide to the Study of Insects*, he reported
the rearing of Isodontia from cocoons found in abandoned
tunnels of a carpenter bee. The cocoons were separated by
bits of rope, and the end of the nest was filled with a tight
wad of sedges. Since that time a number of observers have
noted the unusual nesting behavior of these wasps. There
are numerous species in different parts of the world, and all
of them are rather similar in their behavior. But to this day
the only person to have studied grass-carriers in detail is
Octave Piel, a Jesuit priest who lived in China. Father Piel
was able to induce the wasps to nest in hollow bamboo
stems in great numbers, and by patient observation was able
to learn much of their lives.

The grass-carriers are by no means spectacular in appearance. They are medium-sized, about an inch long, with a
slender body and long wings. Our common species, harrisi,

is all black, but some of the tropical species are variously marked with red or yellow. They are often seen on flowers, and seem especially partial to white sweet clover.

Isodontia is strictly an opportunist when it comes to selecting a nesting site. Almost anything will do as long as it is hollow and about a half-inch in diameter. Abandoned carpenter bee tunnels or other cavities in wood are favorite places. Hollow stems of dead sumacs are commonly used, and one can also sometimes induce them to nest in artificial nests made of glass or wood. Grass-carriers will also nest in the abandoned burrows of mining bees in clay banks. In the Southwest the wasps make use of the leaves of yucca or Spanish dagger, which, when they grow old, roll up so that they form long tubes up to two feet in length. In the Southeast the wasps exploit the most unusual natural cavities of all: the long, tubular leaves of the yellow-flowered pitcher plant, or huntsman's horn. As in all pitcher plants, these leaves are specialized for capturing insects, and have even been known to capture bumblebees. Isodontia merely stuffs the watery bottom of the pitcher with grass or sphagnum moss and proceeds to nest quite successfully in the upper part of the leaves.

Once the nesting site has been selected the work really begins. It is not just a matter of gathering blades of grass indiscriminately and stuffing them helter-skelter into the hole. For the partitions between the brood cells special types of fibers are selected. These may be very fine grasses, strips of epidermis from herbs, various types of woolly plant down, or even—in the case of Packard's wasp—bits of rope. This material is chewed up and pressed into a compact plug. Then, when the cavity has been nearly filled with a series of cells, each separated by a partition of this kind, the wasp begins to gather somewhat coarser strands, which are twisted in such a way as to fill the cavity rather loosely. For this part of the nest the wasps have even been known to use excelsior! Finally, when only an inch or two remain to be filled, long, stiff grasses are collected and stuffed into the entranceway. Eventually these grasses form a broom-like tuft that projects from the hole. It is strange, indeed, to see such a broom of straws projecting from a hole in a clay bank or a hollow twig! The function of this broom is unknown; it is almost as though the wasp were carried away by her own cleverness and artistry. The broom weathers away fairly soon, and one can usually guess how old a nest is by the condition of the straws at the entrance.

When the female Isodontia is after straws for the broom, she flies to tufts of tall grass and examines the dried blades of the older growth. She flies from plant to plant, apparently appraising individual straws for thickness and rigidity. When she finds one that is suitable she walks out to the tip and then back again a certain distance, apparently measuring off the required length. Then she neatly cuts it off between herself and the base of the straw, like the man who saws off the limb on which he is sitting. But in this case the wasp buzzes her wings as she severs the straw, and in a split second she is flying toward her nest with the straw trailing behind.

When the broom is complete, the nest is finished and the wasp may begin another one in a nearby cavity of similar nature. A single nest may contain six or more cells, depending upon the length of the available cavity. Each cell, of course, contains a wasp egg and the necessary provender for the development of the larva. Isodontia is as fastidious about the food she gathers as she is about her building materials; our local species, harrisi, preys chiefly upon tree crickets, delicate green insects that produce shrill, piercing tones from trees and bushes in late summer. Despite their attractive appearance and their musical propensities, tree crickets are justly regarded as pests, for they injure the twigs of bramble and tree fruits by their egg-laying punctures. I found one Isodontia nest which contained nearly forty paralyzed tree crickets, so presumably several wasps might considerably reduce the tree cricket population in a given area.

Now and then one finds an Isodontia harrisi nest which contains a variable number of meadow grasshoppers mixed in with the crickets. The nests in yucca leaves mentioned earlier, which were studied by a noted student of insects, George P. Engelhardt, were found to be supplied exclusively with immature Texas spiny katydids. These katydids live among cacti and other thorny desert vegetation and are rarely seen by man. The adults are three or four inches long and are capable of inflicting a painful bite if handled. Mr. Engelhardt examined forty or fifty brood cells and found that each one contained three or four young spiny katydids. Since there were hundreds of wasps flying around the yuccas, they must have captured in all several thousand katydids.

But it is not so much as a hunter that Isodontia stands out among her clan, but as an artisan. There are some poorly known tropical spider wasps that are reported to line their nests with bits of leaves, somewhat like leaf-cutter bees, as well as some that use bits of moss and vegetable detritus. But I know of none that use grasses, least of all that use a number of different types of grasses, each for a different purpose. But one doesn't have to go to the tropics to study Isodontia; a good back yard will do, and a good pair of eyes and plenty of patience.

A good back yard, too, is the place to study another fastidious builder, the common black-and-yellow mud dauber, Sceliphron caementarium. Sceliphron is a very common wasp, and a good deal more down-to-earth than Isodontia—in a literal sense, since she gathers her building materials from the edges of mud puddles and other places where good, malleable dirt is available. From this she fashions her char-

acteristic mud cells under bridges and under open roofs of
barns, garages, and out-buildings (the passing of the outdoor
privy was a sad day for Sceliphron!). Each cell she provisions
not with crickets and grasshoppers (though she is not unrelated to Isodontia), but with small spiders, especially crab
spiders and the like. Cell after cell is plastered together until
there may be a cluster nearly as big as a fist. Unfortunately
these are a bit unsightly and are not always appreciated by
homeowners, any more than are the wasps themselves, for
all of their elegant wasp-waisted figures and their black and
yellow colors.

Sceliphron has the rare distinction of having had a whole
book written about her: *The Ways of a Mud Dauber*, by
George D. Shafer, a professor emeritus of physiology at Stanford. Shafer found them delightful and friendly wasps, and
was even able to train them to come to his fingers for honey.
To some of his wasps he gave individual names, and watched
the running out of their brief lives with genuine regret. But
he was not deterred by sentiment from chronicling their pri-
vate lives and conducting a few simple experiments upon
them. Being a physiologist, he was particularly concerned
with the curious way in which wasps dispose of the waste
products which accumulate in their bodies during development (a matter which we will return to in a later chapter).
But in the course of his book he also describes how the females
build their cells and lay their eggs, how the larvae spin their
cocoons, and so forth.

As everyone with an eye for such things knows, the black-
and-yellow mud dauber has an equally common cousin, the
blue mud dauber (Chalybion californicum). But the blue
mud dauber is by no means the expert mason that the black-
and-yellow species is; in fact, she seems to be pretty much a
camp follower, taking over abandoned nests of her cousin and
patching them up to suit her needs. It has been reported that

blue mud daubers will sometimes take over recently completed nests of the black-and-yellow species, throwing out all eggs, larvae, and provender in the nest! Perhaps they do this only when there is a shortage of old nests (black-and-yellow mud daubers never use a nest a second time). Actually, there is need for a very careful study of the relationship between these two very common, semidomesticated wasps.

The blue mud dauber may be a bit of a blackguard in one sense, but in another she is something of a heroine. Two workers at the Louisiana State University Medical Center found that blue mud daubers take great numbers of black widow spiders (the only poisonous spiders in the United States). They found nearly one hundred black widows in five nests, while six nests of the black-and-yellow mud dauber contained 147 spiders—but not a single black widow.

But that doesn't by any means complete our roster of mud daubers. In all parts of the country there are several species of the quite different genus Trypoxylon which also build nests of mud and stock them with spiders. Most Trypoxylons nest in hollow twigs and use mud merely for the partitions between the cells. But the largest species, politum, a glossy black wasp with white "stockings" on her hind legs, builds mud nests of a rather striking sort. The female builds a linear series of several cells, smoothing off the outside to form a long tube, then builds another such tube of cells beside the first, then another and still another. The tubes tend to vary somewhat in length, and the total effect is that of a pipe organ: hence the common name of this wasp, the pipe organ wasp. Nests with only a few "pipes" are very common, and now and then one finds a large one, with as many as twenty-five or more parallel tubes. These nests are built in much the same situations as are the nests of Sceliphron; one can look under almost any bridge, more particularly in the South, and find nests of both wasps. The manner of cell construction is quite similar in the two wasps, and both prey upon spiders. But the structure of these wasps and their larvae indicates that they are not at all closely related; in fact Trypoxylon is placed in quite a different section of the digger wasp family Sphecidae from Sceliphron (and its close relative Chalybion). And a little study reveals that there are some important differences in the behavior of the wasps. In fact, there is one feature in the behavior of Trypoxylon that is not shared with any other solitary wasp: the male actually plays a small role in the nesting process, standing guard over the nest while the female is absent.

This largely completes the gamut of wasps that build mud nests around human structures in the Northeast. But turn to other situations and to groups of wasps other than the digger wasps and one finds still others that use mud for their nests. One of them is a small blue spider wasp which Thomas Say, the "father of American entomology," reared from delicate barrel-shaped mud cells over a century ago and named Pompilus architectus (now Auplopus architectus). This little wasp builds its cells primarily in cavities under rocks or logs; the cells are separate but usually attached end-to-end. There are several related species which make similar nests, but they are not commonly met with. Some of them nest in abandoned nests of other wasps, including Sceliphron and Trypoxylon, and even sometimes reuse old paper wasp nests, plastering them up with mud. In the Orient there are some spider wasps that build rather complex mud nests in hollow trees, and some that build freely exposed mud nests somewhat like those of Sceliphron. Here again, of course, we are dealing with unrelated wasps which have come to have somewhat similar nesting behavior. As one might expect, there are striking differences in some aspects of their behavior. For example, when Sceliphron models her clay she does it entirely with her mandibles, but spider wasps bend the abdomen forward and use its tip as a plastering trowel. Also, spider wasps use a single large spider per cell, digger wasps like Sceliphron, Chalybion, and Trypoxylon many small spiders.

If we turn to the remaining major family of wasps, the vespids or plaited-winged wasps, we find still other kinds of mud daubers. Indeed, the vespids are often called "mason wasps" because so many of them use mud either for partitions in nests in hollow twigs or for their entire nest. One of the crudest sorts of mud nests is built by Ancistrocerus waldenii. This small but robust black-and-white wasp nests regularly on and around Wasp Farm. One of her favorite places is a big, jagged rock in our sand pit—a favorite seat of mine when I am watching digger wasps. Ancistrocerus picks up soil from the sand pit, moistens it with her saliva, and builds an amorphous mass of mud cells which fill various crevices in the rock. But an even more favorite place is across the street in the cemetery. The large letters carved in some of the gravestones provide just the right sort of crevices for Ancistrocerus to build in, and after years of nesting activities many a name has been muddied up by the wasps. I have never been much of a believer in cemeteries, but at least they do furnish places for a few birds and insects to live—though most of them are too well kept to be very useful in that regard.

Not all mason wasps build sloppy nests like Ancistrocerus waldenii. Indeed, some of the finest examples of insect architecture are the products of these wasps. Some species make neat little barrel-shaped cells so much like those of some of the spider wasps that they are hard to tell apart. The so-called potter wasps (Eumenes) are famous for the globular, narrow-necked jugs which they attach to twigs. One can always tell the nest of a vespid, however odd it may look or however much like the nest of a digger wasp or a spider wasp, by breaking into it and examining the contents. Being quite unrelated to other wasps, vespids have behavioral peculiarities of their own. For one thing, they always lay their egg in the empty cell, often suspending it from the wall by a slender filament (other mud-users lay the egg on the prey). Vespids prey upon caterpillars rather than upon the spiders dear to Auplopus, Trypoxylon, and Sceliphron. So while the outside of the nest may tell you little, the inside is a giveaway.

But not all vespids use mud for their nests. Those that do are solitary species, apparently the more "primitive" members of the family. These have given rise to more advanced, semisocial and social wasps, all of which build their nests of paper. These wasps have developed the more refined art of chewing up wood pulp and applying it in thin sheets to form the cells and outer covering of a complex, communal nest. Examples of these are known to everyone: the simple, paper comb of the paper-wasp Polistes, and the great nests of the yellow jackets and white-faced hornets. In the tropics there are species which build nests even more marvelous than these; some of them make several kinds of paper, a thin parchment for the combs and a heavy cardboard for the outer walls, sometimes even an "onion skin" to provide "windows" in the walls. But these social wasps we'll consider in a later chapter: they are a world in themselves.

Looking back over the vast array of situations in which wasps build their nests, one wonders if they have left any opportunities unexplored. The ground-nesting species nest in all kinds of soil, but many have left the soil to nest in dead wood, twigs, or even in miscellaneous objects like abandoned snail shells. But to extend their range farther they have acquired the ability to build: many to build houses of mud, one large group to build of manufactured paper, and a few individualists to build of off-beat materials such as leaves or grass. And the various nests assume such a diversity of form that to study them is almost a science in itself. Here is a wonderful example of what biologists call "adaptive radiation":

starting out from very simple nests in the soil (originally from no nests at all), the wasps as a whole have "radiated out" into every conceivable sort of nesting situation, even to the point of making use of the edifices of that johnny-come-lately, man. At least I find it hard to think of many exploitable niches which haven't been invaded by nesting wasps.

Many of these niches have, of course, been invaded by members of quite unrelated stocks of wasps. Almost any old barn is likely to be plastered with the nests of the unrelated digger wasps Sceliphron and Trypoxylon, with the nests of the former being reused not only by Chalybion but also by various spider wasps and mason wasps. Under one stone one may find the barrel-shaped cells of the spider wasp Auplopus, under another stone the very similar cells of a mason wasp. Mud nests, in the broad view, provide an excellent example of another phenomenon well known to biologists: "convergent evolution." Convergence, as it may more simply be called, merely means that quite different stocks of organisms have "converged" upon a similar way of life and in so doing acquired similarities in structure and behavior. The classic example is the whale, a mammal which has invaded the sea and become in many ways fish-like. But open a whale and you will find it has all the organs of a mammal, not a fish. Similarly, many mud nests have a superficial similarity, but open them and they give away their very different builders. The builders of mud nests belong to at least four stocks of wasps: mason wasps (Vespidae), a small group of spider wasps (Pompilidae), and two unrelated stocks of digger wasps (Sphecidae), one including Sceliphron, the other including Trypoxylon. When a way of life proves successful, like as not a number of different creatures will "try to get in on the act"— and some will succeed.

Convergence and adaptive radiation are phenomena which are widespread among living things, and to recognize them often adds a good deal to the study of natural history. If they were universal phenomena, of course, they would be less worthy of note. They are not, as that individualist, Isodontia, well shows. True, Isodontia once "radiated" from the ground-nesting digger wasps, and in so doing lost many of the spines on her legs, and so forth. But having become a grass-user she has radiated no further: all Isodontia behave much alike—none build free grass nests or weave them into oriole-type baskets (though this would surely be within the possibilities of insects which weave such elaborate cocoons). Nor have any other wasps "converged" upon Isodontia. She remains unique, the only wasp to build of grass. Perhaps that is why I have always felt a special kinship with her. Man is, of course, unique in many features, as Julian Huxley and others have so well pointed out. There is no evidence of radiation in man—in fact, the races of man may some day fuse into one—and no evidence that any other creatures are converging toward him. So I like to think that Isodontia and I have a good deal in common.

CAST OF CHARACTERS

Isodontia harrisi: Eye-so-don'-shuh (Greek *isos*, alike, plus *odontos*, tooth) har'-ris-eye (named for T. W. Harris, a pioneer American entomologist).

Sceliphron caementarium: Skel'-if-ron (Greek *sceliphros*, thin) see-ment-air'-ee-um (Latin, a mason).

Chalybion californicum: Cal-ib'-ee-on (Greek *chalybos*, steel, with reference to the steel-blue coloration) cal-i-for'-nik-um (pertaining to California, where this wasp is also abundant).

Auplopus architectus: Oh'-ploh-puss (Greek *anoplos*, naked, plus *peza*, foot, with reference to the smooth legs) ark-ee-tect'-us (Latin, an architect).

Ancistrocerus waldenii: An-sist-ro-ser'-us (Greek *ankistron*, hook, plus *keron*, horn or antenna, a reference to the way the antennae of the male are hooked at the tip) wall′-den-eye (named for B. H. Walden, an eminent Connecticut entomologist).

FOR FURTHER READING

Piel, O. *"Recherches Biologiques sur les Hyménoptères du Bas Yang-tse (Chine). Sphex nigellus Sm." Annales de la Société Entomologique de France*, Vol. 102, pp. 109–54 (1933).

Shafer, G. D. *The Ways of a Mud Dauber.* Stanford, Calif.: Stanford University Press (1949).

CHAPTER TEN

Thirteen Ways to Carry a Dead Fly

Edwin Way Teale, in his *Near Horizons*, tells how he developed an old orchard on Long Island into an "insect sanctuary" by providing a diversity of plants and other natural objects which attract insects—and most of all by living intimately with the many insects present on his plot. Our philosophy on Wasp Farm has been much the same. We have been primarily interested in our wasps, but wasps feed on other insects or on spiders, so we made our home as attractive as possible to insects of all kinds. Mostly we have simply let things stay as they are, except for planting a garden and then competing with the insects (and rabbits and raccoons) for the harvest. We have used few insecticides, and cut no brush except where it tended to overgrow nesting sites of digger wasps. But mostly it has simply been a matter of focus of attention. Each year we have been alert for the first paper wasps starting to build, for the first Astatas storing their stinkbugs in the soil of our garden, for the grass-carriers trailing their straws into crevices in our house.

These—and many others—we could depend upon each year. Then, of course, there were occasional surprises—wasps that showed up suddenly one day and then were never seen again. One June, for example, Gorytes canaliculatus showed up in numbers in our sand pit. Gorytes, a small black-and-yellow wasp, preyed upon bright green leafhoppers, and the females made a pretty spectacle as they glided in with their prey clutched beneath them by their middle legs. In a few days they had disappeared. The next year I waited for them with a new camera and plenty of color film, but they never appeared—that spring or any spring since.

Another time I strolled out into our garden one hot July evening, hopefully looking for some brown silk on our sweet corn. The corn wasn't ripe, but a strange little wasp was plunging periodically into a small hole in the ground next to the cucumbers. So quickly did she plunge into the open hole each time that I was quite at a loss to identify her or the objects she was carrying. The sun was setting, and I was impatient to find out what wasp was invading the domain of our Astatas— for this was a smaller, swifter, and altogether different wasp. Finally, by placing a leaf over the hole, I was able to slow her down long enough to see that she was a Crabro—Crabro advenus, I later found out—and the thing she was carrying was a freshly stung cluster fly, or "buckwheat fly" as they are sometimes called in central New York. In the next few days I found a number of them nesting in the garden and on the edge of the lawn. In every case they left the entrance to their hole open and plunged in quickly with their flies. The flies were always held underneath by the middle legs of the wasp. In the nest-cells the flies were stacked on their backs, four to seven to a cell, with the wasp's egg on the bottom one. One of the nests contained eight cells, with a total of something like fifty flies, most of them cluster flies or Fannia flies. Both kinds of flies are common about homes and gardens, as the former are parasites of earthworms and the latter breed in decaying vegetables.

I never found Crabro advenus again, but they are secretive wasps and may well be nesting every year in some odd corner of the farm. But of fly-catchers there are always plenty. Two of the tiniest of digger wasps, Oxybelus bipunctatum and Oxybelus quadrinotatum, nest in numbers every year in our sand pit. Both are intrepid hunters of flies, and I would hesitate to estimate how many they bury there each year! On any sunny summer's day one can count on watching them perform in their own curious ways. They dig their burrows by standing on their heads and attacking the sand in a most passionate manner. When the nest is finished, they bring in flies so rapidly that one wonders how they have time to go through the routine of hunting, stinging, and grasping them in the appropriate manner. Around our way, quadrinotatum (the larger of the two, almost a quarter of an inch long) takes mostly flies which I myself almost never see in nature—adult root maggots, grayish flies almost as large as the wasp. The

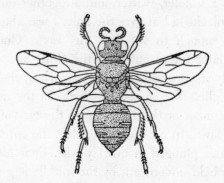

FIGURE 11. A female Oxybelus quadrinotatum.

immature stages of these flies develop on the roots of a wide variety of vegetables; for example, they cause wormy radishes (which we always have plenty of). Oxybelus bipunctatum, a shiny little wasp with two white spots on it, takes a great many kinds of small flies, including midges and mosquitoes. I found one nest packed solid with blackflies!

Oxybelus wasps are so tiny that to study them properly one

has literally to lie with his face in the dirt. But if one is willing to do this he can observe a bit of behavior stranger than
the nearest zoo will provide. For when these wasps arrive
with their flies, the flies stick out behind them, and since the
flies are often nearly as large as the wasp they look like a pair
of small wasps in tandem. The wasps land on all three pairs
of legs, so obviously none of them are used to hold the fly.
If one watches closely and repeatedly he can perceive that the
sting of the wasp is actually inserted into the front part of
the thorax of the fly. Just how the wasp manages to impale
its prey so well that it remains affixed to the sting while it
flies through the air and then lands and digs into the nest is
anybody's guess. Whatever its secrets, Oxybelus is a most efficient wasp, and by carrying the fly in this completely unique
manner has all her legs free for other things. Wasps which
carry the prey with their middle legs (like Crabro and
Gorytes) are fairly efficient too, but when they land at the
nest entrance they somewhat awkwardly stand on their hind
legs only while they open the nest entrance with their front
legs. Incidentally, such wasps shift the prey to the hind legs
as soon as they enter the nest, so that the prey is actually
behind them as they go down the burrow. A few wasps are
known (including some species of Oxybelus) which carry
their prey all the way with the hind legs. Perhaps this is how
the unusual behavior of our local Oxybelus evolved. Once
they may have used their middle legs like many other wasps,
shifting the prey to the hind legs as they entered the nest so
that the two went down the burrow in tandem, thus better
fitting the small diameter of the burrow. A next step may
have been regular use of the hind legs, thereby avoiding the
shift in position on entering the nest. Finally, when the prey
was already well back behind the wasp, held by the hind legs,
a stock of Oxybelus found still a better way to do it: by in-

serting the sting into the fly and releasing the fly altogether from the legs.

As a matter of fact, this is only part of a longer evolutionary sequence. All of the more "primitive" wasps carry their prey with their mandibles, sometimes assisted by the legs. Such wasps often have to set their prey down before they enter the nest, since their appendages are all pretty well tied up. While the prey is lying on the ground, even briefly, it is subject to attack by ants and other predators and also by certain parasitic flies. Thus it is not surprising that many of the more "advanced" wasps have gotten away from this in various ways.

The study of the ways in which wasps carry their prey is a fascinating one in itself. Kunio Iwata, a brilliant Japanese specialist on wasps, once tabulated twelve different types of prey carriage (actually he recognized three major types, each with several subtypes). It might be interesting at this point to list these twelve types and mention a few examples among the wasps we have considered in these pages. The arrangement is roughly from primitive to advanced; that is, we believe that at one time all wasps behaved as in type one, then some advanced to type two, some of these on to type three, and so forth. Only Oxybelus and a few close relatives got to stage twelve.

(1) Drag the prey backwards on the ground, seizing it only with the mandibles. Typical of this level of behavior are many of the spider wasps, which we considered in Chapter Two, as well as some other primitive wasps which we haven't mentioned. This is a cumbersome method: the wasps can't even see where they are going without dropping their prey and turning around!

(2) Carry the prey forward on the ground, seizing it with the mandibles. This is much better from the point of view of getting somewhere in a hurry, but the prey is out in front

where it may obstruct vision or walking. Most of these wasps straddle the prey in one way or another. One group of spider wasps has acquired the ability to amputate the legs of the spiders, presumably so they can be straddled and carried forward without stumbling over the legs. Ammophila, which we discussed in Chapter Six, carries its caterpillars this way, but here the long body and high stance of the wasp are admirably suited for dragging along the caterpillar.

(3) Same as the preceding, but the front legs also used to support the prey. Some Ammophilas and related wasps do this.

(4) Carry the prey forward on the ground, grasping it by the hind legs. No North American wasps are known to do this, and the one known example needs confirmation.

(5) Fly with the prey, holding it with the mandibles. Here belong some spider wasps, all of the social wasps, and such common digger wasps as the mud daubers. I would expect this type to have evolved directly from (2), not by way of (3) and (4). The prey has to be considerably smaller than the wasp for this type to be practicable.

(6) Fly with the prey, holding it with the mandibles and the legs. This is a very common type, exhibited by, for example, Astata (Chapter Four) and Sphex (Chapter Five). When these wasps land at the nest entrance, they usually hold the prey by the mandibles alone, here reverting to the preceding type.

(7) Fly with the prey, holding by the front legs only.

(8) Same, but use both fore and middle legs. These are not common types, and there is some doubt as to whether they occur at all.

(9) Fly with prey, holding it with middle legs. This common type occurs in Bembix, Bicyrtes, Gorytes, Crabro, and many other wasps. As mentioned earlier, the prey is often

transferred to the hind legs as the wasp enters the nest, thus presaging the next two types.

(10) Same, but use both middle and hind legs. A few Crabros and other wasps are reputed to belong in this category.

(11) Same, but use only the hind legs. Only a few Oxybelus and related wasps have reached this stage.

(12) Impale the prey on the sting. Again, a few Oxybelus and related wasps.

One could actually prolong this list by taking another factor into consideration: the part of the prey which is grasped by the wasp (e.g., antennae, legs, thorax). Also, the list omits certain rather special types such as the practice of some wasps of climbing up a stem and then taking flight with their prey, the practice of Anoplius depressipes of dragging the spider over the surface film of water, etc. Actually the whole subject is quite complicated and full of uncertainties: even some of Iwata's twelve basic types need further documentation. But by and large we can say that there has been a progression from simple and inefficient methods of prey transport to more advanced and efficient types, and perhaps Iwata's twelve stages are about as close as we can come to the heart of the matter at this time.

There is, however, one more type to be added to the list, one that Iwata didn't consider because it hadn't been discovered in 1942 when he wrote his paper. This type can confidently be numbered (13), because it is in every way the most remarkable type of prey transport known among wasps.

The story of the discovery of this mode of prey carriage, is, I think, an interesting one. The time was August 1959, the actors myself and several little wasps going by the name of Clypeadon haigi. The setting was an exciting one: a small pocket of sand dunes set in a great valley between the Chiricahua Mountains of Arizona and the Peloncillo Mountains of New Mexico, near the little town of Rodeo and not far

from the place where the Apache chief Geronimo made his
last stand against the whites. There was such a grand sweep
of land and sky that at times it was hard to focus my attention on the wasps I was looking for: certain species of Bembix
which in fact were rather scarce and hard to work with. The
desert was a sea of flowers, the skittering horned toads a
constant source of amusement, and the towering clouds over
the Chiricahuas a periodic cause of concern—and admiration.

Another source of interest were the many nests of harvester
ants scattered across the desert. There were two kinds here:
a pale yellowish-brown species that nested in the small sand
dunes and a dark brown species that nested where the soil
was flat and relatively firm. In each case a few large holes with
a circle of debris around them formed the entrance; there was
no large mound of earth such as the harvester ants of the
Great Plains make. It was while watching the processions of
worker ants going in and out of a nest of the dark brown
species that I first discovered Clypeadon—and once I discovered it I had little time for anything else. One of these small
wasps (superficially reminding me of Crabro advenus of my
cucumber patch) landed beside the column of ants and began
to pivot about, apparently watching the ants. Now I had
never before seen a wasp attack a worker ant—least of all an
aggressive ant such as this was—and at the time I was unaware
that any wasps were known to do this. So I was aghast to see
the wasp suddenly run up to an ant from the side, knock it
over and sting it on the underside, then quickly pick up the
ant and take off. And it picked up the ant in a most peculiar
fashion: by ramming its tail end down between the bases of
the last two pairs of legs of the ant, so that the ant hung on
to the tail end of the wasp upside-down. Perhaps I was seeing
another case of prey carriage on the sting. A perusal of the
literature showed that a related species of Clypeadon had,

in fact, been found to prey on worker ants and to carry them to the nest on the sting.

But certain things bothered me. For one thing, the sting apparatus of Clypeadon is rather weak, hardly sufficient for holding such a large and irregularly shaped insect as a worker harvester ant. For another thing, why did the wasp always ram its tail end into the same rather unusual part of the ant's anatomy (for I later saw this behavior many times)? Another thing that puzzled me was the unusual form of the tail end of the body of wasps of the genus Clypeadon. The pygidium, or upper plate of the tail, was biconcave and had certain incisions on the margins, while the hypopygium, or lower plate, was somewhat similarly modified. Now modifications of the tail ends of digger wasps are almost always associated with hammering the soil in the burrows, for most digger wasps do in fact pound the soil with the pygidium. It had been assumed that the very elaborate pygidia and hypopygia of Clypeadon served a similar purpose, and in fact a related wasp had been named Listropygia (shovel-tail). But it was hard to see what purpose a double concavity and all the other modifications served. Furthermore, when I took a freshly killed female Clypeadon and a paralyzed worker ant I found that I was able to make the double concavity on the pygidium fit neatly around the hind coxae—the basal segments of the hind legs—while the concavities of the hypopygium fitted as neatly over the middle coxae. All that was needed was to assume that the wasp was able to spread the two tail-plates slightly so as to exert pressure against the two pair of coxae— and one had as neat an "ant clamp" as one could imagine. After watching a good many Clypeadons in action I convinced myself that this was, in fact, the case. Of course, it was impossible to be sure whether or not the sting actually penetrated the body also, but I am convinced that the sting can be of little importance in securing the ant. To some extent the various indentations in the plates seem to fit over projections on the ant. In Listropygia, a related subgenus which also preys on harvester ants, there is actually a small terminal knob on the pygidium. This knob fits perfectly into a small concavity in the body wall between the two pairs of coxae, and I am convinced that it serves as still another "gadget" for hooking the ant to the tail of the wasp.

I would imagine that the ancestors of Clypeadon carried their prey on their sting, and that later the pygidium, already somewhat modified as an instrument for pounding soil, underwent various changes and supplanted the sting for carrying the ants. I watched a great many of these wasps carry their ants to their nests, and never saw one drop an ant or pause to readjust one. The ants were quickly grasped, and when the wasps arrived at the nest they entered quickly, the ant being attached so far back that it provided no impediment to opening and entering the nest. A curious thing is that the closest relatives of Clypeadon and Listropygia are members of genera of Iwata's types (6) and (9). The leap to (13) was quite a considerable one, and we can only surmise that the wasps at one time went through some or all of the stages in between.

This is the essence of the story of Clypeadon, but one other facet of it I cannot resist mentioning. Eventually I found quite a few of them, and recorded well over one hundred ants as prey. In every case they represented the dark brown species, even though this species nested apart from the small dunes where the Clypeadons nested. The pale-colored harvester ants nested right in the dunes—in fact the ants sometimes bothered the wasps as they came in with their prey—but the wasps never attacked them! Once or twice I saw a Clypeadon approach a nest of the light species, but they always withdrew quickly. To me the two kinds of ants were very much alike, but to the wasps they were obviously very different.

I found Clypeadon a wonderful little wasp to work with.

Harvester ants are overly abundant and unpleasant creatures anyway! Certain it is that no wasp is likely to surpass Clypeadon in its elaborate and highly efficient method of carrying its prey—unless there is a wasp somewhere that conveys its prey by remote control!

CAST OF CHARACTERS

Gorytes canaliculatus: Go-rite'-eez (Greek *gorytos*, quiver) can-al-ik-you-late'-us (Latin, covered with small grooves, a reference to the grooves on certain parts of the body of this wasp).

Crabro advenus: Crab'-row (Greek, hornet) ad'-ven-us (Latin, visitor).

Oxybelus bipunctatum: Ox-ib'-el-us (Greek *oxys*, sharp, plus *belos*, sting) by-punk-tate'-um (Latin *bis*, twice, plus *punctatum*, spotted, a reference to the two spots on the abdomen).

Oxybelus quadrinotatum: cwa-dree-no-tate'-um (Latin *quadri*, four, plus *notatum*, marked, a reference to the four spots on the abdomen).

Clypeadon haigi: Cly'-pee-a-don (Latin *clypeus*, shield or clypeus, a plate at the front of the head, plus Greek *odontos*, tooth) hay'-guy (named for T. R. Haig, an energetic collector of wasps).

FOR FURTHER READING

Evans, H. E. "A Review of the Nesting Behavior of Wasps of the Genus Aphilanthops, with Special Attention to the Mechanics of Prey Carriage." *Behaviour*, Vol. 19, pp. 239–60 (1962).

———. "The Evolution of Prey-carrying Mechanisms in Wasps." *Evolution*, Vol. 16, pp. 468–83 (1963).

Iwata, K. "Comparative Studies on the Habits of Solitary Wasps." *Tenthredo*, Vol. 4, pp. 1–146 (1942).

CHAPTER ELEVEN

The Lair of the Bee-Wolf

We tend to take August pretty much for granted. Summer has been with us for a while; the foliage has lost some of its sparkle, the bird songs much of their urgency. The meadows glitter with goldenrod, the brambles are hung with blackberries, and the cicadas unwind their souls from the treetops. It is a warm, lazy world, almost too lush, too beneficent, too tranquil—and winter too long ago to remember.

But to a student of insects high summer is no time for dreaming: it is a time for being afoot and alert. The world of insects is at its shrill crescendo, in a few short weeks to fade to a whisper and then to months of silence. But just now every leaf, every blade of grass seems to have its insect denizen, and the night has a katydid to sing to every star. And wasps are now out en masse harvesting the bounty of insects. Hear that cicada stop his song mid-way? Like as not he is a victim of the giant cicada-killer, who will inter him beneath the driveway. And what became of the tree-cricket that used to sing so piercingly from the hedge? Doubtless Isodontia is up to her old tricks. Even the lowly plant lice are not immune, for Pemphredon is about, stuffing them in great numbers into her cells deep in the soft wood of a rotten log.

One of the most characteristic wasps of late summer is

Philanthus solivagus, a slender, medium-sized, black-and-yellow wasp of undistinguished appearance but, as usual, of highly individualistic behavior. On Wasp Farm solivagus appears about the first of August, and from then on to the first frost the females are busy burying bees in local sand banks. They have a predilection for sloping banks, preferably in the neighborhood of clumps of goldenrod, asters, and other flowers. Philanthus—literally, lover of flowers—of course feeds on nectar like most other wasps. But the female has ulterior motives: she is also after the various bees that come to flowers for pollen and nectar. The bee-wolf, the Europeans call a related species. Slipping upon a bee, Philanthus thrusts her sting into its throat before the prey has time to fend off the predator with her own sting—or if she does, the sting merely glances off the heavy armor of the wasp. Apparently almost any bee of small or medium size will do. We took 137 bees from female solivagus a few years ago and found there were twenty-one species involved, mostly various kinds of halictids or "sweat bees." Although certain kinds of cleptoparasitic bees are common enough, they are almost never taken as prey by Philanthus, apparently because they are not pollen-gatherers. But when I collected the 137 bees from Philanthus solivagus I also took six wasps, each of a different species. These were undoubtedly taken on flowers and were, to the Philanthus, more "bee-like" than some of the parasitic bees. Wasps do not often prey upon other wasps, and I know of none in North America that do so regularly.

The European bee-wolf is actually distributed throughout much of the Old World and has become notorious as an enemy of the honeybee. This wasp, Philanthus triangulum, is large enough to handle honeybees well and, in fact, rarely preys upon anything else. In North America, species of Philanthus have been taken preying upon honeybees in Florida, Kansas, and Utah. The honeybee is not native to North America, but was brought in by early settlers. Thus these wasps must originally have preyed upon some of our larger native bees, as in some measure they still do. In Utah, Philanthus flavifrons has been seen to enter an apiary, land on the entrance board of a hive, and "mow down" several of the guard bees before finally seizing one of them and dragging it over the ground. Flavifrons is not an especially large wasp and presumably is unable to carry the honeybees in flight; one wonders if the burrows are large enough to accommodate them. Other Philanthus carry their bees in flight, holding them beneath their bodies by their legs. Normally the bees, whether honeybees or wild bees, are captured on flowers. However, we once saw a female of one of the smaller species, gibbosus, enter the nest of a ground-nesting "sweat bee" and come out with a bee, which she took to her own nest not far away. She did this four times in ten minutes. A rather strange sight, to see a wasp carry a bee out of one hole and plunge into another hole; one wonders how they manage to sting them in the confines of the burrow.

Three species of Philanthus nest on Wasp Farm. Besides solivagus, which nests in sloping or vertical banks, we have gibbosus, slightly smaller and likely to nest in either vertical or horizontal surfaces, and finally politus, a tiny species which nests mostly in flat sand or gravel. The three species not only tend to differ slightly in the situations in which they nest, but they also differ slightly in their season of activity and in the size of the bees they take. Politus appears first (in June) and takes only the very tiniest of bees, solivagus last, and takes the largest bees, while gibbosus is intermediate in both respects. I suppose all these slight differences add up to make them less than complete competitors (as I mentioned in Chapter Four, complete competitors supposedly cannot co-exist). But there is a good deal of overlapping in all these characteristics. On more than one occasion I have seen all

three species nesting simultaneously and virtually side by side.
And I have taken two species of bees from the nests of all
three species. I suspect that both bees and nesting sites are
so plentiful that they do not actually impose any important
limitations on the wasps. But the wasps have plenty of parasites, chiefly small flies that deposit live maggots on the prey.
In situations like this where parasitism keeps the populations

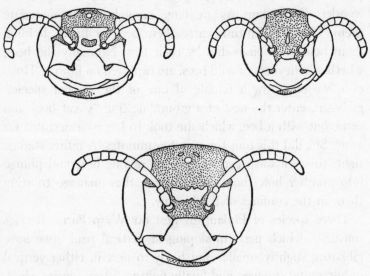

FIGURE 12. Three species of Philanthus (females) seen head
on. They are: gibbosus (*upper left*), politus (*upper right*),
and solivagus (*below*).

at a lower level than the availability of food and nesting sites
would otherwise justify, the CCCC principle may not be so
important. That is, several species may inhabit essentially
the same environmental niche and not really fully occupy it.

I suspect this is the case with these three Philanthus. There
is pretty good evidence of this in the fact that while they do
overlap with respect to prey, nesting sites, and season of activity, they have some very decided differences in certain

aspects of their nesting behavior. For example, the female politus, when she finishes digging her nest, levels off the mound of earth at the entrance very completely, so that the nest entrance is not marked by any telltale mound of earth. Both politus and gibbosus always close the nest entrance when they are away, again making it less conspicuous to parasites. Solivagus does none of these things, but makes such a deep and complex nest that one suspects that the parasites may have their troubles finding the cells. All of the major behavioral differences between the three species appear to be tied up with avoiding parasites, not with avoiding competition with other species of Philanthus. This certainly suggests that parasites have provided the major limiting factors for these species.

Of course, it is hard to judge the real value of these behavioral devices in avoiding parasitism. In the absence of any quantitative or experimental data on the matter, one has to be very subjective: for example, a human can find a nest of politus or dig out the cells of solivagus only with difficulty, so one assumes that parasites may experience similar difficulties. This is hardly "scientific method"; but at the moment I don't know a better theory to account for behavioral differences of this sort.

When I first began to work on Philanthus I worked with politus, one of the commonest wasps on Wasp Farm. I was constantly amazed at how rapidly the females brought in their bees and how quickly they left their burrows again. It turned out that the burrow was very short, only about four inches long, and that the female merely let her bees accumulate in a heap in the bottom of this burrow. Thus she was able to work very rapidly during periods of sunshine. Later, she would go into the nest and prepare her cells, several inches below the bottom of the burrow, and drag the bees into them. Prey storage of this sort is common in Philanthus and related genera, also in Astata and some other wasps. The final picture is that of a short, oblique burrow terminating blindly a few inches down, with the cells below the end of this burrow at a depth of usually about five or six inches.

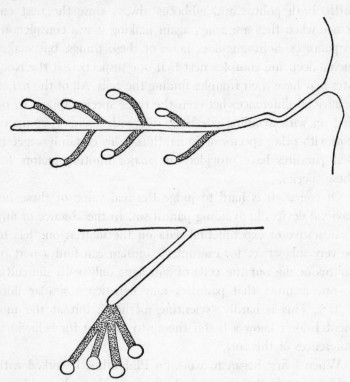

FIGURE 13. Nest profile of Philanthus gibbosus (*above*) and Philanthus politus (*below*).

When, one hot August afternoon, I decided the time had come to spend a little time with solivagus, I was hardly prepared for what I found. The nest entrances were very conspicuous, since they were rather large, always left open, and generally had a pile of sand around the entrance (though this tended to weather away or to roll down the bank). Digging out the nest should be a simple matter, I thought, and I went to it. The burrow plunged into the bank for about a foot, then disappeared. A little deeper I found it again, only to lose it once more. Another nest with the same results, and another. I was afraid I would ruin the whole sandbank and still find no cells, though the wasps had been bringing in bees at a furious pace. Dripping with perspiration and covered with sand, I decided to go home and take a shower

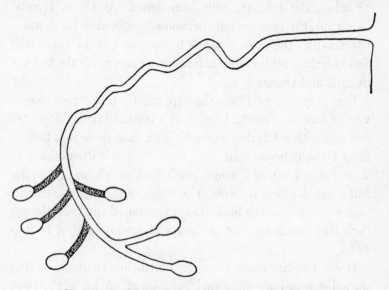

Figure 14. Nest profile of Philanthus solivagus.

and start afresh in the morning. After more failures and half-successes, the pattern emerged. The wasp digs into the bank, more or less perpendicularly to the slope, for about a foot; then she goes straight up for two or three inches, then down and deeper into the bank for several inches, then up again, and so forth. Eventually there may be eight or more such "kinks" in the burrow, each carrying one deeper into the bank, until one reaches a depth of nearly a yard. Believe me, following a burrow only one-fourth inch in diameter for two or three feet into a sandbank is not easy even when the burrow is straight; and the burrows of solivagus are anything but straight. Eventually one finds the cells, but these are well off the main burrow. Apparently the wasp first starts her cells when she is only about a foot and a half from the entrance, then gradually lengthens the burrow and constructs additional cells along the way. Each cell is at the end of a side burrow several inches long, and these side burrows are of course closed off when the cells are fully provisioned. As far as I could figure out, the bees are only occasionally stored in the burrow. More often, the female seems to prepare two or three cells first and then fill them up before laying an egg on the top bee in each and closing it off.

Larger species of Philanthus apparently make even deeper nests. Once, in Florida, I followed a vertical burrow down for five feet without finding any cells. Standing there in a hole so deep I could barely look over the top, and with nothing to show for it, I vowed I would never work on Philanthus again. But I haven't kept my vow. The differences in the nest structure of various wasps have always fascinated me even though their study involves a lot of hard work and no end of frustrations.

It was the European bee-wolf, Philanthus triangulum, that started a now-famous animal behaviorist on his life's work. In the opening chapters of his autobiographical *Curious Naturalists*, Niko Tinbergen tells how, as a student looking for a problem suitable for a doctor's thesis, he first encountered Philanthus on the sand plains of Hulshorst, Holland. There were many wasps nesting there, provisioning their nests with honeybees captured on a nearby heath. By marking individuals with spots of paint, he quickly learned that each wasp maintained but a single nest at a time. He found the nests to be about two feet deep and to contain several cells, each stocked with two honeybees.

Tinbergen was especially intrigued by the problem of how

the wasps locate their burrows. He began a series of studies which eventually extended over several seasons and involved several of his students and co-workers. His experiments are among the most ingenious performed on digger wasps, and I cannot resist a brief account of some of them, even though Tinbergen, in his very readable book, has told the story in more detailed and intimate terms than I can.

Like everyone who studies digger wasps, Tinbergen noted that the wasps, when they finish their nests, fly up and make a series of loops around the nest entrance before taking off—the so-called "locality study." That this was in fact a locality study was easy to demonstrate. While a wasp was away hunting he removed all sticks, pebbles, and other prominent features from around the nest entrance, but left the latter intact. The returning wasp was much confused and found her nest only after twenty-five minutes of trial-and-error searching. When she came out of the nest she made an unusually long locality study, though normally a wasp leaving for the second time makes little or none. This restudy of landmarks after they have been disturbed has been called by some workers the "reorientation flight." Tinbergen found he could not only confuse wasps easily, but he could also mislead them, when there were only a few conspicuous objects nearby, by moving these objects several inches to one side. The wasps generally followed these objects, responding not to the appearance or odor of the nest itself, but to the pattern of landmarks about it.

Tinbergen's next step was to train wasps to artificial landmarks which could be manipulated in various ways, thus enabling the experimenter to learn the relative value of various landmark components. He and his colleagues first trained a number of females to a circle of pine cones around the nest entrance. When the circle of pine cones was displaced while the wasps were away, they would, in most cases, return to the center of the circle of cones rather than to the true nest entrance. This enabled Tinbergen and his co-workers to design experiments involving a choice on the part of the wasp. For example, they trained wasps to circles of alternating cones and flat discs, then moved the cones to one side and the discs to another side, each in a loose circle. Without exception the wasps chose the cones. They also chose pine cones in preference to solid objects such as square blocks or solid cones; these and other experiments demonstrated that broken patterns are chosen in preference to solid patterns. But wasps trained to a circle of pine cones and then given a choice of a circle of solid blocks versus a group of pine cones not in a circle (for example, in a square or irregular pattern) generally returned to the circular pattern. Of course, the original training pattern need not be a circle; one worker trained wasps to return to the center of the "pan" of a "Big Dipper" design. Obviously the arrangement of objects around the nest is memorized by the wasps; the objects involved in the arrangement may be almost anything available, but objects with broken patterns which extend well above the ground are preferred.

Of course, returning wasps cannot see the objects immediately around the nest entrance until they are quite close. During the locality study more distant, larger objects are also memorized: trees, hillocks, and the like. It is more difficult to experiment with these, but enough has been learned so that we can be quite sure that these larger objects and their relationship to the smaller ones close to the nest and to major landmarks still farther distant from the nest all play a part.

It is natural to ask to what extent homing in Philanthus is typical of that of all digger wasps. In a general way, digger wasps are surely much alike; all make locality studies and are guided in large measure by the landmarks they memorize during these studies. Yet there are many differences, depending upon differing nesting situations, altitude of flight, and so forth. Ammophila, which we discussed in Chapter Six, learns her landmarks in flight, then returns to the nest over the ground! In Ammophila, details of the soil surface are of much importance even at some distance from the nest, and such things as paths and furrows are far more important than in Philanthus. Bembix, which we discussed in Chapter Seven, provides still another case, especially those species which nest in extensive dunes devoid of notable landmarks. Another Dutch worker, van Iersel, studied the landmark value of various objects placed near nests of the European Bembix rostrata by timing the reorientation flight of the wasps as they left the nest. He found no correlation of reorientation time with the height of objects or with their width or volume, but only with their total surface. By using cardboard sheets of varying widths, he was able to show that the wasps use rings of landmarks around the nest. The stronger the disturbance to one point in the system, the more they use the undisturbed part of that ring or the next larger one. Thus Bembix is clearly adjusted to the paucity of landmarks in dunes and to the fact that the available landmarks often consist of no more than gentle swellings or depressions in the contour of the sand.

But some digger wasps forage great distances from the nest, sometimes as much as a mile or two. Furthermore, they must sometimes do a certain amount of hunting about over a considerable area. Must such hunting always be done within a framework of familiar landmarks? Unsuccessful hunters often return to the nest periodically, and perhaps these trips serve to reinforce their memories. But beyond much doubt landmarks are not quite the whole story. A great many insects are able to navigate a straight course by maintaining a constant angle between their bodies and the light rays coming from the sun; they may then return over the same course by maintaining the same angle on the opposite side of the body. It is known, too, that many insects are sensitive to the plane of polariza-

tion of light in the sky, and to this they are able to respond
even when the sun is not visible. The compound eyes of insects, consisting as they do of great numbers of complex small
elements, each facing in a slightly different direction, seem
to be particularly efficient organs for utilizing this so-called
"light compass." We humans are scarcely aware of such matters as the angle of light rays and patterns of polarization,
and yet insects and some other "lower animals" are well
aware of them and are guided by them in important ways.

Since the sun is so far away, its rays are virtually parallel
when they reach us. Thus, an insect maintaining a constant
angle with the direction of the sun's rays will fly a straight
course. But if the source of light is close by (for example, a
lamp), its rays diverge sharply, and an insect performing the
light compass reaction near such a source of light may be
carried toward the source of light in a spiral track as it tries
to maintain its constant angle with the direction of the rays.
Thus the classic example of the stupid moth singeing its wings
at a flame is merely another example of man's fouling up a
wonderful behavioral adaptation.

Of course, the trouble with the sun and with patterns of
polarization is that they are constantly moving. If an insect
is to navigate back over the same route it cannot delay long
or its direction may be off by several degrees. But some insects,
including bees and ants, have an excellent sense of the passage
of time and can compensate for the sun's movement by chang-
ing their direction of flight according to how much time has
elapsed. Not much is known about wasps in this regard, but
since ants and bees are both regarded as having evolved from
wasps, surely these abilities must exist in at least rudimentary
form in wasps. My own guess is that the light compass is
fairly important in wasp navigation, particularly in strong-
flying forms that travel considerable distances to find their

prey, but that it most often works jointly with landmark recognition.

All of this points up how very different are the senses and the nervous mechanisms of insects and men. I suspect that when man finds living things on other planets, there will be little there to shock me profoundly. I have been watching Philanthus bury bees in our sand pit for some years.

CAST OF CHARACTERS

Philanthus solivagus: Fill-anth'-us (Greek *philia*, love, plus *anthos*, flower) so-lee-vay'-gus (Latin *solus*, alone, plus *vagus*, wandering).

Philanthus flavifrons: flav'-ee-frons (Latin *flavus*, yellow, plus *frons*, front of the head).

Philanthus gibbosus: gib-bose'-us (Latin, humpbacked).

Philanthus politus: pol'-it-us (Latin, polished, shining).

Philanthus triangulum: try-ang'-you-lum (Latin, triangular, perhaps a reference to the triangular black spots at the base of each abdominal segment).

FOR FURTHER READING

Carthy, J. D. *Animal Navigation*. New York: Charles Scribner's Sons (1957).

Evans, H. E., and Lin, C. S. "Biological Observations on Digger Wasps of the Genus Philanthus (Hymenoptera: Sphecidae)." *Wasmann Journal of Biology*, Vol. 17, pp. 115–32 (1959).

Tinbergen, N. *Curious Naturalists*. New York: Basic Books (1959).

CHAPTER TWELVE

How to Attract Wasps, and Why

Some years ago I read a book by that delightful nature humorist Will Cuppy; it was titled *How to Attract the Wombat* and was something of a takeoff on the many books on how to attract birds. Now I have no objection to birds, or for that matter wombats or other forms of wild life: all are welcome on Wasp Farm. But we have been particularly anxious to attract wasps, and I would be remiss if I did not pass on a few pointers on a subject so vital to everyone. Or would you prefer a chapter on "How Not to Attract Wasps"?

I confess that now and then I would just as soon not attract certain wasps myself. A few yellow jackets add zest to a picnic, but too many make it a bit hazardous—even I don't particularly like to eat wasps. And paper wasps have so much affinity for houses that they are often a nuisance, especially with children around. The stings of these social wasps are not to be taken lightly; the effect may last for some time, and allergic persons often become seriously ill. No, I am content to let social wasps alone, and have even been known to destroy their nests.

But solitary wasps are another matter. The various digger wasps, mud daubers, and dwellers in twigs and rotten wood are a joy to have around. Unlike the social wasps, they rarely make any effort to defend their nest, and most of them can even be handled gently without causing them to sting. I have been studying wasps intimately for twenty years and have been stung only on a few occasions when I handled them roughly, and deserved as much. The sting of solitary wasps may or may not be severely painful, but in any case the effects rarely last more than a few minutes. I would rather be stung a hundred times by digger wasps than once by that darling of the philosophers, the honeybee!

Attracting wasps is not difficult; in fact, it is easier than not attracting them. One merely needs to be lazy. Let the weeds and brambles grow up, and don't prune the roses and fruit trees or cut out dead sumacs and elderberries: the more unkempt vegetation the more insects for wasps to prey upon, and the more hollow or pithy twigs the more cavities for them to nest in. Plow a garden and plant it to interesting things, but don't cultivate too conscientiously and by all means don't go overboard on insecticides: share the wealth with the insects, which after all are mostly attractive and rather amusing (even a worm in the salad provides interesting dinner conversation). Have a decrepit garage, woodshed, or out-house, and spare the paint and fancy new carpentry: many a wasp will use the eaves and various holes and crannies in the walls. And have a few barren places about, where the soil is loose, gravelly, and too poor to support anything but digger wasps.

Of course, if one's zeal is great enough, there are certain positive measures one can take to attract wasps, such as importing a sand dune. A much simpler project is to provide artificial nests for wasps that nest in hollow twigs. These can be crude or rather elaborate, depending upon one's inclination. The simplest type is easily made by taking stems of dead trees and shrubs (sumac is perhaps the best) and cutting them in lengths of six to ten inches. Some should have holes bored in one end, others left with the original pithy centers. They can then be tied singly or in bundles in trees or in the rafters of woodsheds and elsewhere. Certain wasps will use the bored-out twigs, while other kinds will remove the pith and use those twigs. Some, if left undisturbed, will be used over and over again, sometimes by quite different species of wasps.

A somewhat neater type of "trap-nest" can be made by buying one-inch square strips of straight-grained, seasoned pine and cutting them in lengths of about six inches. Then, with a good assortment of long bits, drill a hole in one end of each for nearly the length of the stick. Differently sized bores between one-eighth and one-half inch in diameter attract wasps of different sizes. Trap-nests of this type can easily be mass-produced and scattered about singly or in clusters in trees, sheds, or almost anywhere above the ground, generally in a horizontal position. Filled nests can be spotted easily because the hole will have been closed off by the wasp with a plug of mud or vegetable matter. If one wishes to study the contents, the nest can be split open lengthwise with a jack-knife; the two sides can be put together again and held there by rubber bands. More elaborate types employ narrow sheets of glass beside the boring, the glass being covered by metal or wooden strips. Nests of this type can be examined without having to split the wood, but they are much more expensive to make and apparently sometimes less attractive to wasps. One can also insert a glass tube into the boring in such a way that it can be slipped out for study, or for that matter just use uncovered glass tubing. In general, wasps are more reluctant to accept glass nests and those that do accept them often suffer attacks of mold on the cell contents. Apparently the moisture from the earthen partitions and the cell contents is unable to diffuse through the walls and condenses on the tubing, resulting in a humidity close to saturation, well suited for the growth of molds.

Artificial trap-nests have provided a wonderful boon to

biologists interested in learning about the distribution of twig-nesting wasps and their behavior and that of their parasites. By saturating an area with trap-nests of varying bore diameter, one can obtain an idea of the species of twig-nesters present and the relative numbers of each, how they compete for nesting sites, how they differ with respect to nest structure and type of prey, what parasites are present and which wasps they attack, and so forth. Even a few trap-nests in a back yard provide an interesting spectacle for children and adults alike. Dipogon, the spider wasp of the two beards, is a common nester around Wasp Farm, as is another spider-hunter of an entirely different family, Trypoxylon clavatum. Even an occasional grass-carrier obliges. But the most common users of trap-nests are mason wasps, solitary members of the family Vespidae, and the most common of these is a black, pale-banded species with the mouth-filling but euphonious name Ancistrocerus antilope.

Antilope has been a particular pet of Professor Kenneth Cooper of the Dartmouth Medical School. Cooper, although by profession a cytologist, has for many years studied wasps as a hobby. For an "amateur" he has made some remarkably valuable contributions to wasp biology; his training in another field appears to have given him some unusual insights into the study of wasps. He has trap-nested extensively in several states and encouraged others to trap-nest in still other areas. Out of this has come a series of beautifully executed studies of antilope and other species, a few of which I'll touch on here as an example of what can be done with trap-nests.

But first, a few facts about Ancistrocerus antilope—facts which anyone in the Northern Hemisphere can check on, for the species is common in Europe and Asia as well as in North America. In nature, antilope nests in many kinds of natural cavities, but most particularly in hollow branches of dead sumacs and other trees. The species has also been found nest-

ing in abandoned mud dauber nests, between the shingles of
houses, and in a cavity of the window frame of a shuttle
train running between Bézenet and Doyet, France. The Peckhams even found a nest in the mouthpiece of a tin horn! Trap-
nests with a bore diameter of about one-fourth inch are readily
accepted. Having located a suitable cavity, the female prepares a number of cells in series, the number depending upon
the length of the cavity. Each cell averages somewhat less
than an inch in length, so in a trap-nest with a bore five inches
long there may be about six cells. The cells are separated by
thin mud partitions, and the outermost and last cell is sealed
off with a thick mud plug. Each cell is first provided with an
egg, which is suspended from the roof of the cell near its inner
end. The wasp next captures and weakly paralyzes from four
to fifteen small caterpillars (depending on their size) and
stuffs them into the cell. She then puts up a mud partition
and repeats the procedure with the next cell in line. The
wasp egg hatches in two or three days and the wasp larva consumes the caterpillars over a period of about a week and then
spins its cocoon in the cell. Cocoons spun in early summer
give rise to adult wasps about three weeks after they are
spun, but those spun after about the middle of July do not
yield adults until the following spring.

Some special problems would seem to await the emerging
adult wasps. Since the cell at the far end of the tunnel was
prepared and provisioned first, its cocoon is several days older
than that in the outer cell and ought to give rise to an adult
wasp first. How is the wasp to get out of its confinement, surrounded as it is on three sides by wood and on the fourth side
by a series of cells containing cocoons and separated by mud
barriers? As a matter of fact it turns out that this is not a
problem at all; the order of emergence of the adult wasps is
approximately the reverse of what one would expect: the
younger wasps, in the outer cells, as a rule actually mature

and leave the nest first, making way for the later-maturing wasps in the deeper cells. How is this brought about? Apparently at least two factors work together—and probably other factors that we don't yet understand. For one thing, if a wasp does happen to reach maturity before the wasp in the cell blocking its way out, the wasp may simply wait its turn (at least sometimes and for a certain period of time): apparently the emptying of the neighboring cell provides a stimulus for leaving the nest. For another thing, the wasps in the deeper cells are almost always females, those in the outer cells almost always males, and the females require a few more days to mature: they develop in cells which are (on the average) slightly larger and contain more caterpillars, and the adult female wasps are slightly larger than the males. This seems to be true of many solitary wasps: females are produced in larger cells containing more prey. Wasps, and in fact most Hymenoptera, are to a considerable extent able to control the sex of their progeny. They lay "female" eggs in the larger cells with more food, "male" eggs in smaller cells with less food. Would that we humans were as able to determine the sex of our offspring!

So it turns out that the order of emergence really isn't a problem at all, or rather it is a problem which has been solved by the wasps. Here is another problem: how does the emerging wasp tell "which way is out"? Emerging deep inside a twig or trap-nest, it would seem that the wasp might have only a fifty-fifty chance of going out the right way. If it went the wrong way, it would come to the end of the boring and spend fruitless effort trying to chew its way through the wood. As a matter of fact it is known that wasps headed the wrong way do exactly that, even to the point of dying in the act of trying to get out—even though in most cases the burrow diameter is great enough to permit them to turn around and "try the other way." Furthermore, a wasp which goes the

wrong way in the boring may cut through several other cells
and in its desperate efforts to get out may destroy the occupants of those cells, too. Thus if 50 per cent of the wasps
headed out the wrong way, the number of wasps which
emerged successfully the right way would be considerably less
than 50 per cent. But of course the wasps have solved that
problem too; they could not possibly afford to lose over half
of their numbers in such a manner. It happens that the adult
wasps do not have to "decide" which way is out, for they
emerge from the cocoon facing in the right direction. Cooper
examined 2674 stocked cells from trap-nests of several species,
and found only 14 pupae which were facing in the wrong direction; he examined 234 cells from natural nests and found none
facing in the wrong direction. However, when the larvae are
consuming their caterpillars they move about in various directions, and even larvae spinning their cocoons have to turn
about in order to weave both ends of the cocoon. Yet when
they settle down in the cocoon (as "prepupae," soon to transform into pupae) they do so with their heads pointing toward
the outside of the nest. The critical period is clearly when the
larva is fully fed but before it becomes dormant. But what
provides the information? How does the larva "know" which
way to face?

This problem is of course common to all wasps which nest
in tubular cavities, and it is not surprising that several theories
have been put forward. Gravity has been suggested, but it is
hard to see how gravity could work in perfectly horizontal
nests. Hans Bischoff, a German worker well known for his
important book *Biologie der Hymenopteren*, thought it might
be diffusion of air from the outside. K. W. Cooper proved that
this theory was false by the following experiment. He made up
several trap-nests with a boring all the way through them,
then closed off one end tightly with a cork. As soon as the
wasps had filled these nests, he pulled out the cork and re-

placed it with a loose plug of cotton; at the same time he sealed over the terminal plug of the nest, at the other end, with a material which air would not penetrate. Thus the maturing larvae received their air supply from the opposite end from the normal. Nevertheless when Cooper split open the nests two weeks later he found that all the pupae faced the original nest exit.

After considering several other possibilities, Cooper concluded that the partitions between the cells must convey the necessary information to the mature wasp larvae. Each mud partition is constructed from the outside of the cell, of course, since the female makes the partition after the cell is fully provisioned; a partition which closes off one cell serves as the basal wall of the next cell. Since she works from the outside, the wasp is able to smooth off that surface of the partition, but the inner surface remains rather bumpy. Furthermore, the outer surface tends to be concave while the inner surface is slightly convex. It certainly seems plausible that the partitions might provide the necessary clues to the larva, which would merely need to direct itself toward a rough, convex wall and away from a smooth, concave wall.

Cooper first performed the obvious (though rather difficult) experiment: he carefully reversed the partitions in several nests containing eggs or small larvae. He then waited until the larvae had pupated and discovered that twenty-four of twenty-seven pupae were facing the wrong way, toward the blind end of the boring. Obviously the partitions were crucial in determining the orientation of the pupae. The three pupae which were not "fooled" may have resulted from the fact that it was very difficult to do a perfect job of reversing these delicate and rather crumbly walls.

Most persons would probably be content to let the matter ride at that, but Cooper asked still further questions. Do both walls of a cell serve as guides? If not, which is the important one? Is it the texture of the wall or its curvature that conveys the information to the larva? To answer these questions he had to devise various artificial cell walls. Thin discs of Bristol board were used for smooth, flat walls and the ends of gelatin capsules for smooth convex or concave walls; both of these could be roughened with sandpaper grit. First he inserted discs of Bristol board in front of the face of a series of inner cell walls, then in front of a similar series of outer cell walls. Surprisingly, in both series most of the pupae oriented correctly, even though the larvae were barred from consulting one of the true cell walls. He also reared several larvae in "giant cells," made by removing the walls of several successive cells. Such larvae spun their cocoons against the wall at one end or the other of the giant cell and generally oriented themselves correctly. These experiments answered his first two questions: both inner and outer walls convey information, and either one will do by itself; there is no need for the larva to compare the two walls.

To answer his third question, Cooper made up some artificial trap-nests containing cells with one wall flat and smooth, the other end flat and rough. He transferred small larvae and their caterpillars to these cells and allowed them to complete their development and pupate. Nearly all of them pupated with their heads toward the rough wall. This established the fact that wall texture by itself was important. What about wall curvature by itself? Again he made a series of artificial cells, this time each with one smooth, flat wall and one smooth, convex wall. In such cells about half the larvae directed themselves toward the flat wall, about half toward the convex wall. He then did the same thing, but with one cell wall concave and rough instead of convex and smooth (the other wall still flat and smooth). Surprisingly, most pupae faced away from the concave, rough wall (even though they faced toward a flat, rough wall in the earlier experiment).

Apparently the stimulus provided by a concave wall overrides that provided by roughness or smoothness of the wall; on the other hand convexity of itself is of no particular importance.

Regardless of the details, the remarkable thing is that the female wasp "tells" her offspring which way to direct themselves: she builds information into the cell wall which is "interpreted" by the larva a week or so later. These strictly solitary wasps thus have a simple communication between members of different generations: something which cannot be said even for the honeybee, which is able to say a great deal more, but only to its nest-mates. Yet it is difficult to see how wasps could have invaded this particular habitat without having developed some such method of communication, however unusual it may be.

As a matter of fact, one finds that all twig-nesting mason wasps use the same method of insuring the proper orientation of the pupae. Even wasps of the genus Trypoxylon, of the family Sphecidae, "speak the same language." Cooper obtained several Trypoxylon nests, cleared out the contents, and transferred to the cells young larvae and prey of Ancistrocerus antilope and several other mason wasps. The pupae oriented almost perfectly in the nests of these very unrelated wasps. Certain cuckoo-wasps, parasites of mason wasps and quite unrelated to them, also respond properly to the signals built into the cell wall. If they did not, they might themselves experience high mortality and scarcely would persist as successful parasites.

This brief summary by no means does justice to Cooper's many fine studies based on trap-nest material; indeed, his studies of the mites that live in association with Ancistrocerus antilope read almost like science fiction. And he is not the only person to have extracted all sorts of new information by the simple techniques of trap-nesting. A naturalist need not wax dreamy-eyed about the tropics when his back yard or wood lot can yield so much excitement!

CAST OF CHARACTERS

Ancistrocerus antilope: An-sis-tro-ser′-us (Greek *ankistron*, hook, plus *keras*, horn) an-til′-oh-pee (Greek, a horned animal).

Trypoxylon clavatum: Try-pox′-ill-on (Greek *trypa*, hole, plus *xylon*, wood) clav-a′-tum (Latin, clubbed, a reference to the club-shaped abdomen of this wasp).

FOR FURTHER READING

Cooper, K. W. *Biology of Eumenine Wasps.* Part I: "The Ecology, Predation, and Competition of Ancistrocerus antilope (Panzer)." *Transactions of the American Entomological Society*, Vol. 79, pp. 13–35 (1953). Part II: "Venereal Transmission of Mites by Wasps, and some Evolutionary Problems Arising from the Remarkable Association of Ensliniella trisetosa with the Wasp Ancistrocerus antilope." *Transactions of the American Entomological Society*, Vol. 80, pp. 119–74 (1955). Part V: "Digital Communication in Wasps." *Journal of Experimental Zoology*, Vol. 134, pp. 469–514 (1957).

[12] Bembix pruinosa emerges from her nest in the heart of a sand dune. She scrapes sand into the entranceway with her two front legs working synchronously, a manner of digging characteristic of most of the true digger wasps. When she finishes the sand will be perfectly smooth, yet when she returns to the nest, she will be able to find it without hesitation in this vast landscape of sand.

[13] A miltogrammine fly perches on a twig overlooking a digger wasp nesting site. These flies are tireless enemies of wasps, forever watching for opportunities to deposit small maggots on the wasps' prey. Almost any kind of wasp or prey will do. In the cell the maggots grow rapidly, often killing the wasp's egg or larva or, at the very least, competing with it for the available food. Certain kinds of miltogrammines follow females laden with prey and deposit their maggots on the prey before it is placed in the nest, while other kinds actually enter the nest and place their larvae in the cell.

[14] The egg of Bembix spinolae in place on a bee fly. The vast majority of wasps lay their egg on their prey, and most species of Bembix first capture a fly, then place it at the far end of the cell and glue their egg upright to the side of the fly. Only when this egg is ready to hatch, in about two days, will additional flies be added to the cell. A few species of Bembix (such as pruinosa) omit the fly and merely deposit the egg in the empty cell.

[15] Clypeadon laticinctus entering her nest with her prey, a worker harvester ant, fastened to the end of her abdomen. This wasp is able to use her mandibles and all three pairs of legs for entering the nest, but most other wasps employ the mandibles and/or some or all of the legs for holding the prey.

 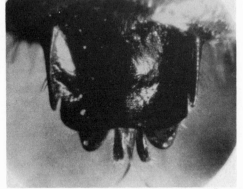

[16] "Tail views" of two wasps photographed through a microscope reveal striking differences, yet these two wasps are closely related. In Aphilanthops, on the left, the pygidium (or "tail plate") is simply a flattened triangle which is used for pounding soil into the burrow when filling it. In Clypeadon, on the right, the pygidium is greatly modified for fastening onto the legbases of the ants which serve as prey. Note the rather weak sting protruding behind the pygidium.

[17] Philanthus politus is one of the commonest of digger wasps over much of the country. Although a member of the "bee-wolf" group, it does not impress one with its ferocity, being mild-tempered and not much over a quarter of an inch long. This female has just brought in a small bee, left it in the burrow, then come out very quickly, closing her nest behind her.

[18] A nest of the pipe-organ wasp, Trypoxylon politum. Each of the parallel strips in the walls represents a load of mud. There are well over three hundred such strips in this nest, but this one of three pipes is relatively small, some having been found with over twenty pipes. Each tube contains several cells, each stocked with spiders. The wasp in the cell in the lower center has emerged through a round hole in the wall of the nest.

[19] A worker yellow jacket takes flight from the mouth of the hole leading to the paper nest. This nest, in a rock garden near our back door, was the scene of constant coming and going throughout the late summer, workers carrying out soil to expand the cavity, other workers bringing in wood pulp to expand the nest or food for the larvae. A few days after this picture was taken, the nest was dug out and destroyed, presumably by a skunk.

[20] A "trap nest" tied to the branch of a pine tree. Such trap nests are easily made by boring a hole into one end of a small piece of soft, straight-grained wood. This one has obviously been used by a wasp, for the end has been sealed off with a plug of mud. The nest can now be collected and split with a knife in order to study its contents. The stick can then be sealed together again with transparent tape and put aside to await the emergence of the next generation of wasps—and often of their parasites as well.

[21] The "trap nest" is split open to reveal the four-celled nest of a mason wasp. In this case the contents are a giveaway, for Symmorphus is the only common mason wasp to use the larvae of leaf beetles as prey. The egg of the wasp can be seen at the inner end of the outermost cell (arrow). The two innermost cells were apparently completed several days earlier, for the larvae in these cells have eaten all the prey and are ready to spin their cocoons.

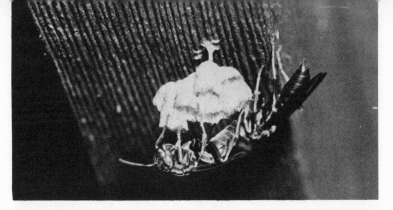

[22] Two Polistes wasps rest on a small nest suspended from the rafters of the garage. This nest, consisting of about ten cells, most of them not yet drawn out to their full length, is about average for early June in the northeastern states.

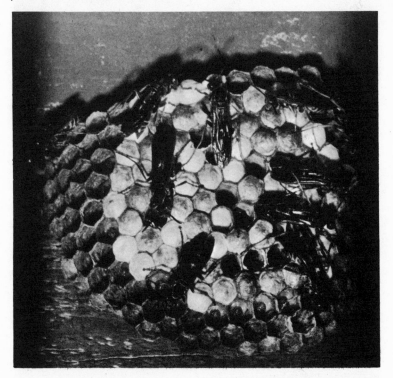

[23] A Polistes nest in August, filled with larvae and with capped cells containing pupae. The uncapped cells distributed among the capped cells have already given rise to the new generation of workers, some of which are resting on the comb. Some of these cells are being used a second time, and eggs or larvae can be seen in most of them.

[24] Steniolia obliqua, a western relative of Bembix, spends the night in great clusters. This cluster on a sunflower head contained over one hundred wasps, about half of each sex, and weighted the sunflower so that it hung low over the grass below. The function of these clusters is unknown—they certainly aren't needed for warmth, and most wasps do well enough without them. Most of the more advanced wasps, such as Bembix, spend the night in their nests.

[25] Humans are not the only creatures with housing problems. Did the wrens fail to return or did the Polistes wasps get there first and make it uncomfortable for the wrens? These are prosperous times for paper wasps, which once had to compete with birds and bats for the available space in hollow trees. Now they are almost entirely inhabitants of human structures.

CHAPTER THIRTEEN

The Social Register

Life is full of frustrations, large and small: and small ones
repeated continually are as bad as large ones. I would hate to
say how many times I have been introduced to someone as
an authority on wasps only to have the person remark: "Oh,
you must come and see the wasps in my attic!" It is a sad fact
that to most people the word "wasp" conjures up an image of
only one particular kind of wasp, the common black paper
wasp. It is understandable that to such persons my enthusiasm
for wasps seems perverted. Polistes fuscatus, the black paper
wasp, is interesting enough in its own way, but will hardly
rate as beautiful or sweet-tempered. And here in the temper-
ate zone, Polistes is hardly a "typical" wasp, being an invader
from the tropics and one of our very few "social" wasps: that
is, the nests are communal affairs, in which several females
live together and exhibit a division of labor. But no book on
wasps would be complete without a chapter on Polistes and
other social wasps, and this is it.

Polistes fuscatus is our most domestic wasp, even more so
than the mud daubers, which also nest in the eaves of buildings but which spend the cooler months of the year dormant
in their nests. The social wasps are different in that they overwinter as adult wasps in various sorts of protected places.

Since Polistes fuscatus generally nests about human habitations, it is natural enough that in the fall those individuals that are seeking a place to hibernate get into houses. Here they may loaf about in the bathroom or perch precipitously over the baby's crib, causing much more concern than is really justified. They can, of course, sting, but at this season they are sluggish and have no nests to defend, so it takes a great deal of provocation to get them to sting. Throughout most of the winter they are rarely in evidence, though on unseasonably warm days they may creep out of their crevices and fly about in the house or even out of doors. By late February and March they are more often in evidence, and by late April those that have survived the winter have begun their nests. Apparently these overwintering females often revisit their old nests on these winter and early spring flights, and when they are ready to build they often return to the same area where they themselves were reared. But they never reuse an old nest, even though they might save themselves a great deal of labor by so doing.

FIGURE 15. A worker Polistes fuscatus.

On Wasp Farm, we usually have a few Polistes nesting under the eaves on various parts of the house. But the major nesting areas are under the garage roof, at each end, where there are vents which provide convenient flyways for the wasps. During some springs I have numbered the various nests here and marked some of the wasps with colored spots so that I could keep track of them. Then I have kept records of individual nests, starting very conscientiously in late April or early May, then tapering off when it came time to grade final examinations in late May and early June, and finally giving up altogether with the great flux of solitary wasps—my true loves —in mid-June. But I have studied them enough, and have read enough about them in books, to know that there are many riddles to be solved concerning these most common of all wasps.

Although the wasps which invade houses in the fall include males and females, the only ones to survive the winter are some of the hardier females which developed late in the season and mated at that time. They emerge from hibernation with live sperm stored in their bodies and with their ovaries beginning to swell, shortly to begin producing eggs which, as in all insects, will be fertilized just as they are about to be laid. At first these females seem to "loaf about" in the sun, visit their old nesting sites, and in general try the patience of naturalists who, also recently emerged from hibernation, are eager to read the book of nature. But one fine day things begin to happen: a few females begin scraping the surface of old boards and logs, chewing up and moistening the pulp, and applying the first blobs of it to the spot they have selected for a nest. At first a small disc is prepared, then a slender pedicel extending downward from it, finally a small cup facing downward. The paper made by paper wasps is remarkably tough stuff, as anyone knows who has tried removing or dissecting the nests. This one small pedicel may eventually hold a flat comb of many cells. But at first there will be only one, then two and three very short cells. By this time the female will have begun laying her eggs; one egg is glued into the bottom (or top, I suppose, since the cup is inverted) and only later is the cell expanded to its full length by the addition of further paper. A small nest with about three cups, one or more of them with eggs, is about par for the first week of May in our area.

By this time the picture is already becoming a bit confused. Here and there one finds a basal disc that was never drawn out into a pedicel, a pedicel that was never expanded into a cell, and small abandoned nests of one or a few cells. And suddenly a second or even a third or a fourth female shows up on an established nest. Up until about the first of July, the picture is a fluid one: females shifting from one nest to another, disappearing mysteriously, abandoning nests, starting new nests, and so forth. Yet some of the nests persist and grow. Their growth is not steady: a week of rain, and nothing much happens; then a couple of warm, sunny days and the nest is suddenly several cells larger. In general, the number of active, growing nests becomes somewhat narrowed down by June. A typical nest in early June may have about fifteen cells, attended by perhaps four or five females, one or two of which may have been on the nest for quite some time, the others more recent arrivals. On each nest one female, often the original founder of the nest, will "stay put" most of the time and do most of the egg laying (we suppose, though this is hard to prove). The others will be in and out, making paper, building cells, and bringing food for the growing larvae. The primary female—this major and perhaps sole egg-layer, often also the founder of the nest—is often called the "queen," the other associated females "workers." The queen and workers differ not at all in appearance, and even their behavioral differences are not spectacular. Unless one has marked the individuals in a nest and watched the nest almost continually, he may be hard put to decide which is the queen. Some workers may spend much time on the nest, and the queen may be away for short periods; all individuals perform various manipulations of the cells and their contents and react to each other in various ways.

An Italian worker, Pardi, studying the European species Polistes gallica, has described a definite hierarchy or "peck-order" among the females on the nest. The female on top of the peck-order dominates the others psychologically, employing various threatening postures, and thus wrangles food from the others and is able to remain on the nest most of the time, develop larger ovaries, and become the major egg-layer. The next one down the peck-order, just as in a flock of chickens, is able to dominate all but the queen, and if the queen dies she quickly assumes the queen's role. The wasps at the bottom of the peck-order presumably lead a rather harried existence and never get to lay an egg. If one kills all the wasps on a given nest and dissects out their ovaries, he finds that the queen has large ovaries full of eggs, the next one down the peck-order slightly smaller ovaries with perhaps a few developing eggs, the next one still smaller ovaries, and so on.

This makes a very nice story, but the fact is that hardly anyone who has studied Polistes has found it to be quite that simple and clear-cut. Even if there is an element of truth in the "peck-order" theory, it leaves many things unexplained. Once a hierarchy has been set up, the dominant wasp can perhaps wheedle the most food and thus develop larger ovaries. But how does the queen acquire her original psychological dominance? Is there a real tie-up between ovary size and behavioral dominance, and if so what is it like? Why do some females establish a nest, where they are "boss," then suddenly leave it and become an underling on another nest? What is the real significance of the various behavioral interactions between the females on the nest? To what extent do the individuals second and third in the hierarchy contribute to egg-laying, and if they contribute at all can one really use the terms "queen" and "workers"?

I remember once, when I was discussing social insects before a group of undergraduates, one of them spoke up and asked: "Dr. Evans, how does a honeybee get to be queen?" What a stupid, naïve question, I thought. Like asking why the sky is blue. But come to think of it, why is the sky blue? And how does a honeybee, or a Polistes wasp, get to be queen? The question is simple, the answer complex and uncertain.

The honeybee is a rather different matter. But in the case of Polistes, I would venture to guess—without any proof at all—that success in hibernation is tied up with many of these matters. Females go into hibernation with a certain limited amount of stored fat in their bodies, fat that will in part be converted into ovaries and eggs in the spring. A wasp that spends the winter at an optimum temperature and is not lured out time and again during the winter may emerge in the spring in prime condition. On the other hand a wasp that is badly chilled or is exposed to occasional periods of warmth, making her more active, may emerge in the spring with the fat in her body depleted and unable to produce large ovaries. In one area there will be a whole gamut from vigorous females, because of their developing eggs ready to start nests and "assert their dominance," all the way down to females which have barely survived the winter—and of course some that haven't. Some of the females in between the two extremes might start nests but be unable to maintain them long, so would abandon them and join other groups of females. But this is all quite theoretical, and even if it should prove true, it still leaves many things unexplained.

Along about the first of July, in our area, the picture changes considerably. About this time the first capped cells appear on the nests; that is, some of the cells have convex, whitish tops on them. This means that the first larvae have reached maturity and become pupae. In a few days the first of the new wasps appear. These will all be females: as we saw in the preceding chapter, wasps can control the sex of their off-spring, and in this case all develop from "female" eggs. These females will have a "new look" about them; they will be a little brighter and lack the tattered wings and worn mandibles of the original occupants of the nest. They will also average slightly smaller, perhaps because they didn't get fed quite as well here, in the spring, as their mothers and aunts did last summer. These females have small ovaries and, of course, don't have any sex life at all, since there aren't any males around. They remain with the nest and assume the duties of paper-making and brood rearing; there is no question that we can safely call them "workers." By the time the new workers begin to emerge in numbers, the females of the elder generation have begun to become depleted in numbers. The hierarchy, such as it is, will often have shifted many times, and if there have been many deaths a female well down on the "peck-order" may now be queen, her ovaries now well-developed and productive. Such a colony may, by mid-July, be a thriving community of a few "elders" and thirty or more new workers. The comb may now be quite large, with perhaps fifty to one hundred cells. But from now on the nest will not grow very much if at all. Unlike solitary wasps, the social wasps may use the same cell twice or even three times. The builders become housekeepers, cleaning out old cells, and the eggs and young larvae, which were once found around the edge of the comb, are now found in the middle, in combs which have been used before.

With this large group of workers, freed from the need to build new cells, hunting in the lush world of midsummer for the caterpillars and other insects which, chewed up into a ball, provide the food of Polistes, it is natural that the larvae are very well fed. The wasps which begin emerging in August are, in fact, a bit larger than those that emerged earlier, and they have much more stored fat in their bodies. And some of these are males, for the old queen has, for some time, been laying some unfertilized or "male" eggs. As the end of summer approaches, the old queen becomes senile and finally dies, the workers lose their attachment to the nest and begin to die off, too. The larger females which emerged in August and early September fly about, feed at the flowers of goldenrod, and mate with the males. It is these females that will survive the winter—some of them anyway—to start the cycle over again in the spring.

Social wasps, as you can see from this rather sketchy account, are vastly different and more complicated creatures than solitary wasps. And yet Polistes has hardly gotten into the social register; its societies are of a very primitive sort as compared to those of some other insects. True, the nests are communal affairs in which there is a division of labor and in which females feed larvae which are not their own offspring— the true test of a "social" animal. But some say that insects must have a "caste" system in order to be considered truly social. This means that there have to be on the one hand "workers" and on the other hand "queens." Now the first group of females to emerge from Polistes nests are, on the average, a bit smaller than the others, and we can perhaps call them "workers" even though they are otherwise no different from Polistes emerging at other times. But later there will be a slight increase in their size, and finally a crop of females that will mate and survive the winter. Should we call all these "queens," and if so, where shall we draw the line? A good many will, of course, fail to survive the winter; are these then disqualified as "queens"? Of the ones that survive, some will not found nests or will abandon their incipient nests to join other groups of females; in these groups, some will lay eggs consistently, others perhaps occasionally, others perhaps later in the season, some perhaps not at all. When is a queen not a queen? When she is a worker, I suppose. But it's a rare day in June that you can put your finger on a Polistes and say: This is a queen. Come to think of it, putting your finger on a Polistes isn't a particularly good idea anyway.

Luckily, for purposes of comparison, we have right around us some wasps that have reached the very apogee of the social evolution of wasps (though no wasps can be said to rank with the honeybee or the ants as social creatures). I am referring to the hornets and yellow jackets. The words "hornet" and "yellow jacket" both apply to the truly social wasps (subfamily Vespinae); there is really no need for two terms, as hornets are merely large yellow jackets (which may or may not be yellow), or conversely yellow jackets are merely small hornets. The term hornet is usually applied to the white-faced hornet, a native wasp which builds large paper nests in trees and bushes, and to the European hornet, a recent arrival from the Old World which often nests in accessible places between

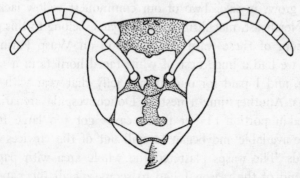

FIGURE 16. Head of a worker yellow jacket, Vespula maculifrons.

the walls of houses. The latter, a huge orange-and-black creature, now ranges throughout most of the northeastern states. The more familiar yellow jackets are best known as unwelcome visitors to picnics; there are several common kinds, some of which nest above ground and some below ground. In every case the nest consists of a series of horizontal combs, one above the other, all of them enclosed in a surrounding carton made up of several layers of paper. These wasps are all rather similar in their over-all biology, but they differ in several ways from their distant relatives, Polistes.

As in Polistes, only mated female hornets and yellow jackets survive the winter. They hibernate chiefly beneath the bark of logs, where they can sometimes be found in midwinter, completely rigid and apparently "frozen stiff." But warm days in March and April slowly bring them out of their torpor, and by May they are out hunting for a place to start a nest. The species of Dolichovespula will start their nest on the branch of a tree or bush. The commonest Dolichovespulas in the Northeast are maculata, the white-faced hornet, and arenaria, a common yellow jacket. The species of the closely related genus Vespula seek out cavities in the ground, chiefly old rodent burrows, later expanding these by digging as the nest grows in size. Two of our commonest yellow jackets in the Northeast, maculifrons and vulgaris, belong to this group. All four of these wasps are common on Wasp Farm. One year we had a huge nest of white-faced hornets in a currant bush, and I paid for our currant jelly that year with a few stings. Another time a nest of Dolichovespula arenaria in a closed-in portion of our porch eaves got too large for the space available and began to spill out of the crevices in the boards. The wasps plastered the whole area with paper; at the end of the season I had to scrape off all the paper and repaint the entire area.

Although the nests of these wasps are eventually much larger and rather different than the nests of Polistes, they start out in much the same way. The female, having selected a place to nest, makes a small basal disc of paper, then a pedicel, and finally several cells in a flat comb at the end of the pedicel—almost exactly like a new Polistes nest. But at some point during or immediately following the construction of these initial cells, the wasp does something different: she builds a paper envelope from the pedicel completely around the cells, leaving an opening in the bottom. This envelope will eventually consist of several partial or complete layers of paper. Having done this, the female ceases to do any more building; she lays eggs in the cells, and when they hatch she feeds the larvae with chewed-up insects. The larvae apparently develop more rapidly than they do in Polistes; soon there are capped cells in the nest, and shortly thereafter the first new wasps appear. These wasps are females which are very much smaller than their mother, the queen. They immediately begin to feed the remaining larvae and expand the nest so that the queen may have more cells in which to lay eggs. From now on until the end of the season the queen becomes strictly an egg-layer; she is fed by the workers and rarely if ever has occasion to leave the nest. Incidentally, one never finds two or more mated, overwintered females working together in the same nest as one does in Polistes. It is not uncommon to find incipient nests which have been abandoned, but in these cases the queens have presumably died or built another nest somewhere else. As in Polistes fuscatus, the nests are strictly annual affairs, never used a second year. However, individual cells may be used two or more times during the same season.

In the hornets and yellow jackets, there is never any question as to which is the queen and which the workers. The queen is very considerably larger than the workers and even shows minor differences in structure; in some species she even has a decidedly different color pattern. The first workers to be produced are very small, since the queen has to feed the larvae herself and doesn't overdo it. After the workers take

over the feeding of the larvae there is a slight increase in
their size, though they still are much smaller than the queen.
Late in the season, the workers build some unusually large
cells, and feed the larvae which develop in them a correspond-
ingly larger amount of food. The wasps which emerge from
these cells will be queens. About the same time the old queen
lays unfertilized, "male" eggs, in either large or small cells,
and thus a crop of males (called drones) is assured. After
mating, the new queens enter hibernation and those that survive are ready to start things off the following year.

At the height of its activity, in July and August, a hornet or
yellow jacket colony has all the hustle and bustle of a great
city. A large nest may have many hundreds, even thousands
of workers. One large nest in California was found to have
4768 workers and a queen at midseason; this nest contained
over 10,000 cells, most of which had been used more than
once, and would surely have had more cells added. The life
of the workers is fairly short, so the population at any one
time is much less than the total population for the whole
season. In the northeastern states, most nests have only a few
hundred workers at their peak. A surprisingly large number
of queens and drones, sometimes several hundred, are produced in late summer. After these leave the nest, the workers
begin to behave erratically, and soon there is a complete break-
down in the social structure of the colony, even though there
may still be several weeks of warm weather ahead. The workers often consume any larvae remaining in the nest and spend
much of their time wandering about, feeding on dropped fruit,
decaying meat, and so forth. The old queen has by this time
died, and the new queens, after mating, seek out places in
which to spend the winter, even though the first frost may
not yet have arrived. Generally speaking, the species that build
aerial nests tend to have smaller colonies which break up
sooner; the subterranean nests of Vespula maculifrons and

other species are often very large and may persist into early fall.

As can well be imagined, a prodigious amount of labor is involved in the gradual expansion of the small "queen nest" into a massive city of paper. A series of combs is constructed, each new one attached to the one above it by several pedicels. As new combs are added, and as the combs are enlarged by adding cells at their periphery, the paper carton surrounding them has of course to be continually enlarged. The wasps do this by simply tearing down the inner layers of paper and adding others at the outside. The outer envelope of aerial nests such as those of the white-faced hornet normally contains many layers of tough paper. If such a nest encounters an obstacle, such as another branch, as it expands, it simply envelops it. Subterranean nests, protected from the elements as they are, have thinner surrounding envelopes and are made of generally weaker paper. As subterranean nests grow, of course, the wasps have to dig out the soil around them to provide room for expansion. It is a common sight to see great numbers of yellow jackets flying out of a hole in the ground, each carrying a small load of earth which is dumped on the ground some distance from the nest.

With these insects, there is no question of whether or not there is a "caste" system: the queen is larger than the workers and differs to some extent in structure and color—and surely in behavior. The workers also show a marked division of labor among themselves; the younger ones stay in the nest, receiving food and paper from the older field workers and distributing it within the nest. If anyone doubts that these are highly efficient and thoroughly social creatures, let him disturb the nest of a yellow jacket! The stings no longer play an important role in paralyzing and preserving the prey, which is macerated with the mandibles; they function primarily as weapons for defending the colony. And even man, the lord and master of the world, must admit that the stings of social wasps are not to be taken lightly.

The common yellow jacket, she who licks up the jam at picnics, is very much the elite of the wasp world. Even in the tropics and in the far corners of the earth there are no wasps that have achieved a higher social organization than these back yard urchins. And we still know very little about the inner workings of their societies.

CAST OF CHARACTERS

Polistes fuscatus: Po-list'-eez (Greek, founder of a city) fuss-cate'-us (Latin, blackish).

Dolichovespula maculata: Dol'-lick-o-vesp-you-luh (Greek *doli-chos*, long, plus Latin *vespula*, a little wasp) mak-you-late'-uh (Latin, spotted).

Dolichovespula arenaria: ar-en-air'-ee-uh (Latin, of sand).

Vespula maculifrons: Vesp'-you-luh (Latin, a little wasp) mak'-you-li-frons (Latin *macula*, spot, plus *frons*, front of head).

Vespula vulgaris: vul-gar'-is (Latin, common).

FOR FURTHER READING

Duncan, C. D. A *Contribution to the Biology of the North American Vespine Wasps*. Stanford, Calif.: Stanford University Press (1939).

Michener, C. D. and M. H. *American Social Insects*. New York: D. Van Nostrand Company (1951).

Richards, O. W. *The Social Insects*. New York: Philosophical Library (1953). (Reprinted in 1961 as a Harper Torchbook.)

CHAPTER FOURTEEN

Why Rabbits Have Long Ears

To him who in the love of Nature holds
Communion with her visible forms, she speaks
A various language . . .

The nineteenth century was the era of the great naturalists:
Cuvier, Lamarck, Humboldt, Lyell, Westwood, Lubbock, Darwin, Wallace, Huxley, Gray, Agassiz, Haeckel, Fabre, and in
somewhat different realms Wordsworth, Thoreau, even Beethoven. The twentieth century belongs to the laboratory scientists. In a review of Isaac Asimov's *The Intelligent Man's
Guide to Science* (1960) we are informed that "biology is a
system that proceeds from biochemistry to the associated subjects of neurophysiology and genetics. All else . . . is stamp
collecting." Natural history, the review makes clear a bit later,
is most definitely part of the "all else."

If this is so, I can lay no claim to being a biologist. And it
seems unfair to call me a stamp collector when I can never
remember what it costs to send a postcard. The truth is, I
find Darwin, Gray, and Fabre worth emulating in this twentieth century. I should like to think that the eloquent lines of
Bryant quoted above, written in 1811, are part of man's
permanent heritage. As a matter of fact I find twentieth-

century man not wholly unresponsive to nature. He may find himself condemned by scientist, poet, and businessman alike. But there is something in the nature of man that will—I fervently believe—always respond to the croak of a frog, to the majesty of a towering cumulus cloud. And there are things to be learned about even the homeliest of creatures, such as the common paper wasps we discussed in the last chapter.

There is not—nor ever has been—room for sentimentality in natural history. Or for ignorance: For every man owes it to himself to be reasonably well informed on the subjects that interest him. We should read the great naturalists and try to grasp their sense of wonderment, their mode of marshaling facts to support new concepts. The modern naturalist is better informed, for he stands on the shoulders of giants; he also has the help of technological advances such as the camera and the computer. Perhaps he will never propose a great theory or found a new field of investigation. But to gather well-documented facts which add to the sum total of human knowledge is in itself a noble thing. It need not be wasps—though wasps and their relatives the bees and ants provide a fertile field—it might equally well be fungi, field mice, or tardigrades. There are enough unsolved problems in an average back yard to keep a battalion of naturalists occupied for their lives.

Even isolated bits of information may take a small but significant place in the annals of natural history. I have a brother-in-law who is an engineer but who once made some unique observations on snakes and published a note on them. A man in New Jersey once cleaned out some light globes and noticed some unusual dead insects in them. They eventually got to me, and I described from them a new species of wasp which represented the first known North American representative of its group. Don't let anyone tell you this is stamp collecting. Each bit of sound information that finds its way into print is duly added to the great body of knowledge about the natural world. That body of knowledge is held together, organized, and rendered significant by the central and unifying concept of all of science: evolution. It is evolution—cosmic, molecular, biological—that lends significance to all our knowledge of the world. It is the concept of evolution that supplies the why—not in any metaphysical or teleological sense, but in the sense of "how come": When and where did a particular structure or behavior pattern arise, what were its antecedents, and what is its biological function? Why do trees have leaves, why do rabbits have long ears, why do wasps sting? Because each is the product of a particular line of evolution, molded continually and in several ways by environmental circumstances down through long periods of time.

The title of this chapter is really just a gimmick; I am not really going to explain why rabbits have long ears. But I would be remiss if I did not attempt a few answers on the why of wasps: Why do they sting, why do they do thus and so. So far I have spent most of this book introducing the characters, and now I have only a few pages left in which to outline the plot: that is, the evolution of wasps, their structure, their behavior, their nests, their social relationships. This is a very big order and you will be disappointed to see how sketchy the plot turns out to be. But that is characteristic of studies of evolution: Human records go back only to yesterday in terms of the history of life on earth, and we are left to reconstruct the history of living things from scraps of information gleaned here and there in nature. But that is half the fascination of such studies: We see small, dimly lit fragments of vast landscapes and try desperately to reinforce our images with additional fragments.

There are, of course, such things as fossils, which provide us with more direct information on the structure of groups at a more or less specific time in the past. Alas, there aren't

enough fossil wasps to tell us very much. But they do at least
assure us that modern wasps are the product of a very long
period of evolution. The first Hymenoptera occurred in the
early Mesozoic era, contemporaneous with the earlier types of
dinosaurs, close to two hundred million years ago. These were
sawflies, a group more appropriately called by the Germans
blattwespen, or leaf-wasps. Adult sawflies are wasps which
are not at all "wasp-waisted," that is, their body is rather
uniformly thick throughout. The females have, at the end of
their body, a saw-like device which is used to cut slits in
plants; the eggs are laid through this device (called an ovipositor) into the slits. The larvae look and act very much
like caterpillars, feeding on leaves, chiefly, even today, of more
primitive types of trees. A few groups of sawflies have larvae
that bore in stems or the wood of trees.

Not too much later, in the middle of the Mesozoic era,
the first of what we call the "parasitic Hymenoptera" appeared, and in considerable variety. These insects are more
wasp-like, for there is a strong constriction or "waist" near
the middle of the body and the ovipositor is slender and
thread-like or needle-like. The parasitic Hymenoptera undoubtedly evolved from sawflies, but the intermediate stages
are lacking. Perhaps the best clue is provided by the stem
sawflies. These insects more or less "stand on their head"
when they force their ovipositor into the stems of grasses and
other plants, and as an adaptation for this they have a partial
constriction in the middle of the body so that they can
"jackknife" themselves appropriately; also, the ovipositor is
quite slender. The larvae, being internal feeders, have lost
their color pattern and most of their appendages.

The larvae of parasitic Hymenoptera feed upon other insects. Some species feed upon only one or a few kinds of insects, others on a considerable variety. In every case the larva
consumes only a single insect, feeding first on the fat and

other non-vital parts, later hollowing out the entire body. Of course, these insects really aren't parasites if one defines a parasite as an animal that develops on another one without killing it, tapeworms or lice, for example. The parasitic Hymenoptera are really a rather special type of predator, the adults seeking out prey not for themselves (though sometimes as a matter of fact they do feed on the prey a bit) but for their progeny. Also, true predators feed upon a succession of prey, but the larva of a parasitic hymenopteron feeds upon only one. For the purist, who can't in clear conscience call these insects either parasites or predators, the name parasitoid has been invented.

Whatever you call them, they are remarkable, abundant, and efficient creatures. The females hunt out a suitable insect, thrust the ovipositor forward, and lay an egg in or on the prey. The "wasp waist" is a very important part of the mechanism, enabling the insect to wield the ovipositor readily in several directions. The ovipositor is often so slender that the egg has to be greatly squeezed to pass down it. The first parasitic Hymenoptera certainly did not paralyze their prey, but later some groups developed modifications of certain of the glands associated with egg-laying such that they produced a paralytic substance. These Hymenoptera were then able to "tranquilize" their prey long enough to lay their egg and take a few sips at the blood exuding from the wound. Some of these insects—certain ichneumons, for example—can inflict a weak sting if one handles them. From its very inception, the sting has been used secondarily as a weapon of defense. But it is worth remembering that this is a secondary function; the primary function is for paralyzing the prey. Only in the social wasps—also in bees, which don't prey on other insects anyway—has the sting become primarily a weapon of defense.

Here, incidentally, we have explained a common why in evolutionary terms: Why is it that only female wasps sting?

Because the sting evolved from the ovipositor, a structure found only in females. It is also interesting that quite a few male wasps have developed a "pseudo-sting," that is, a stout terminal spine (with, of course, no poison glands attached). They wield this spine in defense much as a female wields her sting and can even prick lightly with it. This structure and associated behavior has doubtless had much survival value for the males, for the average enemy doesn't wait to find out whether he is up against a female with a sting or a male with a pseudo-sting. I know I don't!

The larvae of all higher Hymenoptera spend their lives attached to or actually inside a sack of food, and in the course of evolution they lost their eyes, antennae, legs, and various behavior patterns associated with food-getting. But they had to develop some special adaptations before they could function effectively. For example, they could not defecate without fouling their food unless they worked out some sort of special device. The device was simply not to defecate. The larvae of all parasitic Hymenoptera, and of the wasps, bees, and ants which later evolved from them, do not even have a connection between their stomach and their rectum. The undigestible parts of their food simply accumulate in the back part of their digestive tract, and after they have finished feeding and spun their cocoon they void all this material at once. The urinary waste products, which in insects are removed from the blood via special tubules and then poured into the hind gut and out through the rectum, also have to be held inside the body. The urine is stored in the form of white pellets of insoluble uric acid, which can often be seen through the body wall of wasp larvae. This material is not actually eliminated until the first few days of the adult life of the insect. The insoluble uric acid first has to be converted by enzymes to a soluble form, so it can pass into the excretory tubules, then back into insoluble pellets before it is voided. The full story of these remarkable functional adaptations is told by George D. Shafer in his book *The Ways of a Mud Dauber*.

But we have forgotten about the fossil record. The first true wasps do not appear in the fossil record until the last of the dinosaurs had left the scene, some sixty million years ago. But these wasps are of such an advanced type that we can be sure they had antecedents which occurred much earlier. How do "true wasps" differ from "parasitic Hymenoptera"? The most important change has to do with the ovipositor, which has well-developed poison glands and has become so consolidated into an injection apparatus that the eggs no longer pass through it, but have to be laid directly from the body. The most primitive types of true wasps lack many of the specializations of the bulk of the parasitic Hymenoptera, so we know they came from early, unspecialized members of that group. But they behave much like some of them: the female seeks out her prey, stings it into temporary paralysis, lays her egg, and goes her way. The egg is always laid externally and the larva develops externally, feeding through a hole in the body wall. The prey recovers from paralysis, but dies as soon as the larva developing on it begins to consume its vital organs. There was originally no "nest" at all. However, very soon there appeared types of wasps that stung their prey into a more permanent type of paralysis. But such deeply paralyzed prey could not escape other enemies or unfavorable temperature or moisture conditions. Another step therefore occurred at about the same time: The wasp dragged the prey into some sort of protected situation, such as a hollow twig or a hole in the ground. Such were the crude beginnings of the elaborate nesting behavior patterns of solitary wasps and, on still a higher plane, the great colonies of the social wasps.

By the middle of what geologists call the Tertiary period, at the time of the formation of Baltic amber and of the beautiful fossils in volcanic shale at Florissant, Colorado, many groups of wasps, both solitary and social, were well developed. This was roughly thirty million years ago, and we can safely say that no really important advances have been made since that time. Of course, we know nothing directly about the behavior of these early wasps, but we do know something of their structure, and from this we can deduce some things about their behavior. For example, the social Hymenoptera preserved in Baltic amber had well-defined worker castes, which could only have been produced by certain advanced and elaborate behavioral devices.

It is worth remembering that the wasps inherited most of their more important characteristics from their progenitors, the sawflies and parasitic Hymenoptera. These include their general body form and closely consolidated ovipositor, later to form the sting; the body constriction that is so important to wielding the ovipositor; the elaborate hunting behavior, which has its beginnings even in the sawflies, most of which are selective feeders; the reductions in larval structure and special mechanisms for excretion in the larval stage; the ability of the female to lay either fertilized eggs which produce females or unfertilized eggs which produce males; and so forth. Realizing these things, it is not so difficult to arrange the wasps of the present day into a rather indefinite series from "primitive" (most like their progenitors) to "advanced" (most different from their progenitors). For example, it seems a safe generalization that the earliest wasps were rather weak stingers and paralyzed their prey only temporarily. Later, more powerful poison glands evolved and paralysis of the prey was permanent. Still later, the social wasps developed the practice of chewing up the prey and feeding it to the larvae in a ball, at the same time releasing the sting to become a more effective weapon of colony defense. The sting of hornets and yellow jackets even has barbs on it, though these are not as large as in the honeybee. Wasps can sting repeatedly, though the honeybee loses its sting in the wound and therefore cannot sting again. As most everyone knows from experience, the whole sting apparatus of a worker honeybee stays in the wound, and the muscles of the poison sacs continue to contract and force poison into the wound. This is the ultimate in the evolution of the sting.

We can also assume that the first wasps used a single prey for each larva. The parasitic Hymenoptera do this, as do the wasps that rank as primitive on other grounds. A spider wasp, which uses a single spider per cell, is, on this basis, more primitive than an Ammophila that uses two or three caterpillars, and the Ammophila in turn more primitive than a Bembix that uses thirty-five flies. Primitive wasps are also apt to prey on creatures that are themselves primitive, spiders and grasshoppers, for example, since these were available at earlier geologic periods than the flies that Bembix preys upon. We can also assume that simple nests are more primitive than complex nests; the original wasps, after all, made no nests at all. And, as we outlined in Chapter Ten, simple types of prey carriage preceded the more elaborate types found in some digger wasps.

Thus, by establishing and adhering to certain criteria, we can draw a good many tentative conclusions about the evolution of wasps and about the origin of certain specific components of behavior. These criteria might be summarized as follows: (1) degree of similarity to typical, unspecialized parasitic Hymenoptera, (2) degree of similarity to groups of wasps exhibiting structural and behavioral simplicity, (3) evidence from the fossil record of the antiquity of wasps and their prey.

But wasps, like most other creatures, are pretty complicated. Furthermore, they have been evolving through millions of years and successions of environmental situations which we can only dimly grasp. It is little wonder that application of these criteria sometimes doesn't answer all our questions; often it answers them ambiguously or even falsely. It is easy to find wasps that makes simple nests but prey on advanced types of insects and carry them in special ways—Bembix spinolae, for example. Then too, there are wasps which make rather fancy nests but are primitive on most other scores—the mud daubers, for example. There are wasps that make no nests at all and yet must be regarded as highly evolved, for example, the cleptoparasites we considered in Chapter Three. One has to sum up all that is known about the structure and behavior of the creature, then compare it carefully with what is known about other, similar wasps. By using many different features, one can often weed out those that might otherwise be deceptive. Continually, of course, one is bothered by the fact that so little is known about so many wasps!

We have already mentioned "convergence" in connection with mud nests in Chapter Nine; many quite unrelated wasps have taken to using mud for construction, often making rather similar nests. (On the other hand, all the paper wasps probably evolved from a common ancestor.) Convergence may involve almost any aspect of the structure or behavior of a wasp, and can be detected only by a careful summary of characteristics as indicated above. Several features of an animal may exhibit convergence, but if the animals are really unrelated "the truth will out": the majority of the more basic features will show important differences. Both Bembix and Crabro carry their prey with their middle legs, and both prey upon flies. Yet a summation of the total structure and behavior of these wasps suggests that this may be convergence. There are many instances where the issue is not so clear. Both Astata and Philanthus store prey in the burrow. I suspect this is convergence, yet there are certain resemblances in the structure of the larvae of these two that make me wonder.

One also has to watch out for reversals in evolutionary

trends. By and large, wasps which sting the prey lightly are primitive, yet there is evidence that this is not always so: Some groups which now exhibit temporary paralysis of the prey may have evolved from groups that exhibited permanent paralysis. Certain groups of wasps which have no sting at all, such as the cuckoo-wasps, apparently evolved from groups with a powerful sting. Progressive provisioning, that is, the practice of bringing in prey from day to day for the growing larva, is clearly advanced. Bembix not only exhibits progressive provisioning but appears to be derived from wasps which had already achieved progressive provisioning. Yet a few years ago I discovered a species of Bembix that does not provision progressively, but rather fills up the cell with flies and closes it permanently on the same day the egg is laid. After a careful evaluation of all the facts, I decided that this Bembix was not especially primitive for its genus and must have evolved from a type that once provisioned progressively. Here was a very likely case of a reversal of a trend, a wasp that returned to a more primitive type of behavior: And there must be many such cases.

This particular wasp, Bembix hinei, nests on sea beaches in Texas and Louisiana, where it takes advantage of an incredible supply of horseflies in the neighboring marshes. But beaches are precarious places to nest; they are subject to tide action and to storms which toss waves high on the beach, change the contour of the sand, and leave debris all over the place. The Bembix nests in the firm sand around or somewhat above the normal level of high tides; the species is not adapted for nesting in the soft sand behind the beach proper. Progressive provisioning hardly seems practicable in this situation, since it involves a slow provisioning of a single cell over a period of days. But Bembix hinei must nest quickly while the seas are calm and the tides not excessive. Actually, the females work very rapidly, building several cells from a single burrow and often provisioning and closing off two or more in one day. The larvae grow rapidly and spin their cocoons a few days later. The cocoons are presumably impermeable to sea water, though from time to time some of them must surely be washed out of the sand and out to sea. The advantage of progressive provisioning is presumably that the mother remains with her offspring for several days and affords them some protection from parasites and predators. But here on the sea beach Bembix hinei nests alone—except for the ghost crabs—and there seem to be few if any parasites or predators around. Under the circumstances, the importance of speed in provisioning apparently outweighed the importance of this protection, and the species "evolved backward" in this regard.

I speak of the precariousness of the beach habitat from some experience. In June 1956, I camped with a friend for several days on a Texas beach in order to study these wasps. The first two days went well, and we gathered much data and had marked many nests with stakes for further observation. Then, on the third night, we were awakened about midnight by a tremendous storm. The wind was so strong we had to hold up the tent pole manually, but eventually it went down anyway, putting a hole in the roof, leaving us lying on the beach in a crumpled tent with rain coming down in a deluge and waves rushing at us unpredictably. We learned the next day that winds had approached ninety miles per hour in Galveston. The beach was completely changed, my stakes all washed away, and in fact the whole nesting area washed about and covered with debris. The active nests were apparently destroyed, but one has to assume that some cocoons survived, for storms of this kind occur sometimes several times a year in this area. We ourselves obviously survived, but for a considerable part of the night I questioned that we would.

At times, you see, I am willing to put up with a good deal to gather a few facts. My colleagues the laboratory biologists—

who by their definition are *the* biologists—would doubtless
join forces with many a non-biologist in calling me foolish
and misguided. Personally I find the drama of evolution ab-
sorbing above everything else. I am happy to do whatever I
can to put a few pieces of a very large and complicated puzzle
in place. What is most frustrating about evolutionary biology is
not convergence and reversals in trends, but simply too few
facts. The world is full of creatures which have not yet been
given names, a few that have not even been seen by man. We
know relatively little about even most of our commonest animals. The honeybee has been the most popular of insects down
through the years, and there are many books about it. Yet a
host of investigators are still working on various aspects of its
complex social behavior, and they are by no means running
out of new discoveries. Digger wasps may be less complicated,
but there are thousands of species and only a few investigators.
I am not likely to run out of problems, or to ever get to the
problem of why rabbits have long ears.

FOR FURTHER READING

A reader who has persisted to this point will surely be interested
in some of the fascinating recent books on the honeybee. Here are
four of them.

Butler, C. G. *The World of the Honeybee.* New Naturalist Series.
    New York: The Macmillan Co. (1954).
Frisch, K. von. *Bees: Their Vision, Chemical Senses, and Lan-
    guage.* Ithaca, N.Y.: Cornell University Press (1950).
Lindauer, M. *Communication among Social Bees.* Cambridge,
    Mass.: Harvard University Press (1961).
Ribbands, C. R. *The Behaviour and Social Life of Honeybees.*
    Hapeville, Ga.: Hale Publishing Co. (1953).

CHAPTER FIFTEEN

The Long Road to Failure

As we have seen, the first true wasps made their appearance somewhat more than sixty million years ago. Probably they evolved from the parasitic Hymenoptera during the same prolonged period during which the flowering plants emerged as the dominant types of vegetation. Most adult wasps rely upon the nectar of flowers for their carbohydrates. A few of the more specialized wasps and of course all the bees, which evolved from the wasps, use nectar and pollen to feed their larvae. The evolution of flowers is tied up closely with that of the Hymenoptera, a fact that is reflected in the varied structure and chemistry of flowers and in the varied mouthparts of bees and wasps and the pollen-collection apparatus of bees. The majority of wasps prefer flowers with shallow corollas and an abundance of nectar. Flowers of the carrot family are especially favored—a reason why I always encourage wild parsnip and Queen Anne's lace around our place. Some wasps (Bembix, for example) have elongated mouthparts which effectively probe flowers with deep corollas.

I sometimes wonder what Wasp Farm may have looked like at the time of the first appearance of wasps. As one looks around now, the hand of man is most in evidence: cleared fields, second-growth woods, a garden, a lawn, a house, and a garage. Looking a little deeper, one sees the abundant signs of glaciation: soil full of stones of mixed sizes and types, a sand pit representing an old delta into a glacial lake, in the distance a valley deeply gouged out by glacial action. But all this happened yesterday in terms of geologic time. Much earlier one would have found the country to be a vast plain, at times and places grassy, at other times and places forested with very different sorts of trees than occur here now. The flowering plants would be very different and much less in evidence; one would miss, say seventy million years ago, the great splashes of goldenrod and purple asters that now adorn our hills. Woodchucks and song sparrows would be almost as much a dream of the future as man himself. Some of the great reptiles might be in evidence, perhaps even a pterodactyl to take the place of our red-tailed hawk. But the insects would not be so different; there would be grasshoppers, beetles, midges, and a host of others differing only in details from the ones we are used to. Parasitic Hymenoptera—ichneumons and the like—would be much in evidence, and the first true wasps would be hunting out beetles, grubs, spiders, and the like and dragging them into crevices in the soil.

It is hard to be sure just what those earliest wasps were like and just how they behaved. Of our modern wasps, perhaps they were most like the Tiphiidae, rather sluggish black wasps which hunt out grubs in the soil, sting them into temporary paralysis, lay their egg, and go their way. Now and then they find their prey out of the soil, and when this happens some of them are capable of dragging it into a hole of some sort.

Of the wasps we have discussed in these pages, there isn't much doubt that the spider wasps (Pompilidae) represent the most primitive level of behavior. It is hard to believe that they have changed very much in many millions of years. All of them prey upon spiders, which have been around and relatively unchanged for a very long time. All of them use a single spider per cell and many of them paralyze the spider so lightly that recovery from paralysis is complete or nearly so within a few hours. Most spider wasps make a nest only after having subdued a spider, and the nest is usually of a very simple sort. And when transporting the spider, most of them simply grasp it with the mandibles and proceed blindly backward.

That doesn't mean that any living spider wasp is entirely typical of what wasps were like fifty or sixty million years ago. Some species of Anoplius, which we discussed in Chapter Two, may come reasonably close. Anoplius virginiensis and Anoplius depressipes don't even make their own nest-holes, but use pre-existing holes in wood, surely typical of a very early stage in wasp evolution. Yet both are selective feeders, taking spiders of rather specialized sorts. Other species of Anoplius are more generalized predators, but most of these do dig their own very simple nests. And of course the spider wasps have developed a good many specialized lines: types that make multicellular nests, even mud nests; types that carry their spiders in special ways. Some Oriental species are even semisocial, living together co-operatively in hollow spaces in trees. But even these more specialized spider wasps have a distinctly limited behavioral repertory. For example, contact between mother and offspring is ruled out by the fact that only a single spider is used per cell; it would hardly be practicable for the mother to feed a single spider to her larva over a period of a week.

Turning to the digger wasps (Sphecidae), one can hardly fail to be impressed by the remarkable diversity in nesting behavior. To a much greater extent than the spider wasps, the sphecids have burst the bounds of their primitive beginnings. The more primitive living digger wasps center around Sphex, the genus of the Great Golden Digger and the Great Black Wasp (Chapter Five). One "poor relation" of Sphex, the genus Priononyx, includes strictly solitary forms that hunt out grasshoppers, sting them into a state of rather shallow paralysis, then dig a simple, unicellular nest which will contain but the one grasshopper. Thus they are hardly any different from typical spider wasps. Sphex shows several advances: The nests are dug before hunting begins and are multicellular, with each cell being supplied with more than one grasshopper. The species of Sphex also tend to be rather gregarious. Isodontia, another relative of Sphex, has come to exploit hollow twigs and to use a most unusual building material—dried grass. Also belonging to this same general complex are the common mud daubers, Sceliphron and Chalybion (Chapter Nine).

Thus, right in this one complex of rather good-sized digger wasps (the subfamily Sphecinae), one finds quite an array of behavioral traits, primitive to fairly advanced, with Sphex standing somewhere in the middle. But there are certain primitive features that run through this entire group. None of them have any special mechanisms for carrying their prey: They simply pick it up with their mandibles and either drag it over the ground (Priononyx) or fly with it (most of the others). All prey either on grasshoppers and their relatives or on spiders —creatures that have been around and relatively unchanged for a very long time. All members of this group, when closing their nest, ram the soil in place with blows of the front of their head. Most other digger wasps use the tip of the abdomen for this purpose, and many of them have modifications of the last abdominal plate which enable them to do this more effectively.

Ammophila, the so-called tool-using wasp, also belongs to the Sphecinae, though to a somewhat different branch of the subfamily that has come to specialize in caterpillars. The species of Ammophila agree with Sphex and its relatives in most respects, but they stand out for the remarkable ways in which they close their nest, as we discussed in Chapter Six.

Some species of Ammophila use only one large caterpillar per nest, others several smaller caterpillars. A few species bring in their caterpillars over a period of several days; the egg hatches in the meantime and the mother wasp actually has some contact with the growing larva, receiving stimuli from the larva which tell her how much food is needed. A European species of Ammophila is known to maintain two or three nests simultaneously, checking each nest daily and supplying the needed food in each. The genus Ammophila includes some very remarkable wasps which merit a great deal more study.

Another major complex of digger wasps centers around the genus Bembix. These are much stouter and more compact wasps than the Sphecinae, and they prey on rather small insects and use many of them per cell. They carry the prey with their middle legs and, when closing their nest, pound the soil in place with the tip of their abdomen. Bicyrtes, a genus which we met in Chapter Four, uses stinkbugs as prey, but most members of this complex employ more advanced types of insects. Flies are commonly used, less commonly butterflies or moths. All members of this complex build the nest before hunting begins, most of them provision progressively, and many of them spend the nights and all their "idle hours" inside the nest—something even the more advanced Ammophilas do not do. In some species of Bembix, the mother wasp even cleans the debris from the cell, as we have seen occurs in pruinosa (Chapter Seven). And surely pruinosa deserves special mention for several unique features in its nests. Also, pruinosa and several other species have made another important behavioral advance: They lay their egg in the empty cell, before any prey has been introduced. All other digger wasps place the egg on the prey, a holdover from their parasitic ancestors. But in advanced digger wasps such as Bembix the prey is usually killed by the sting, and by the time the egg hatches the original prey in the cell will not be in a particularly good state of preservation. By withholding provisions until just before the hatching of the egg, these wasps attain a higher level of efficiency.

Related to Bembix is that remarkable little beachcomber, Microbembex (Chapter Eight). By becoming a scavenger, Microbembex has entered an entirely different mode of life and left its parasitic progenitors very far behind. But Microbembex is a unique phenomenon. If other digger wasps had followed suit, the sphecids might have become much more versatile with respect to food and even challenged the ants as scavengers and omnivores. But the ants are an ancient group and probably got there first.

With the species of Bembix that nest in great aggregations, make relatively deep and complex nests, clean the cells, and withhold provisioning until the egg hatches, we reach what is perhaps the most advanced type of nesting behavior in digger wasps. In such nests there is much contact between mother and larva. A Chilean species of Bembix is reported to make a multicellular nest in which several larvae are reared simultaneously. This is getting very close indeed to becoming "social." Yet so far as is known no female digger wasps ever live long enough to see their offspring emerge; thus there is no opportunity for the development of a mother-daughter cooperative system.

There are, of course, various types of advanced behavior which occur in certain digger wasps but not in Bembix. Storage of prey in the burrow, for example. This occurs even in Astata (Chapter Four), a relatively lowly digger wasp on most accounts. It also occurs in Philanthus and several related genera (Chapter Eleven). Of course, the storage is quite temporary, but by no means comparable to the storage of food in the nests of many ants and bees. We have already reviewed the different types of prey carriage (Chapter Ten) and found that the most advanced types occur in Oxybelus and Clypeadon. Clypeadon and its relative Philanthus build complex nests and prey upon the very highest of insects—ants and bees.

The family Sphecidae includes several thousand species belonging to more than a hundred genera. There is a great deal we don't know about the evolution of the group. There are many fine examples of adaptive radiation, examples of apparently related genera and species coming to exploit their environment in different ways. There are innumerable examples of convergence, particularly in nest type and type of prey. Then there are curious anomalies here and there, like the cleptoparasitic genus Nysson we discussed in Chapter Three, and like Microbembex. But by and large we can discern a gradual progression from primitive to more advanced types of behavior. It is often instructive to think of behavior in these terms, though of course every species presents its own particular mixture of characteristics, some apparently primitive, some advanced, some ambiguous. It is hardly fair to Sphex to say it is "more primitive" than Bembix. Each occupies its own particular niche in nature, and if Sphex preserves a few more of the characteristics of its ancestors, it is because these characteristics have served it well down through the ages.

The remaining major family of wasps, the Vespidae, we have considered only rather briefly in these pages (in Chapters Twelve and Thirteen). The vespids are structurally very different from sphecids, a little less so from pompilids; they are believed to have arisen from very primitive wasps as a stock independent from the spider wasps and digger wasps. The vespids are not diggers but builders, a fact reflected in their structure, for they have relatively short and non-spiny legs but often rather specialized mouthparts. However, some of the most primitive vespids do dig nests in the ground, betraying an ancestry from wasps closely associated with the soil. One would expect primitive vespids to lay their egg on the prey in the cell, but as a matter of fact no living vespids do this: They all lay the egg in the empty cell, before any prey is introduced. Presumably some ancestral vespids did lay the egg on the prey, but such types are now extinct. Even the most primitive living vespids employ mud in their nests, even those that dig in the ground. Many wasps of this group have taken to nesting in hollow twigs. Here the mud serves them well for the plugs and partitions and for conveying certain important information to the larvae, as we saw in Chapter Twelve. Other vespids build free mud cells, some merely plastering them irregularly in crevices in rocks, others building barrel-shaped cells in clusters in various crevices, still others—the potter wasps— making well-formed jug-shaped cells on the twigs of trees. Most of these mason wasps prey upon caterpillars, which they paralyze by stinging; they normally fill the cell up with caterpillars and close it with a mud plug soon after the egg is laid.

In Africa there are certain mason wasps not unrelated to Ancistrocerus which have embarked upon some interesting new channels of behavior. One species is said to fill its mud cells with caterpillars in the usual manner except during periods when food is scarce. At these times the female lays her egg and then brings in caterpillars slowly over a period of days, as she can find them. One might say that this species employs "optional progressive provisioning." But a closely related species always provisions progressively and furthermore is said to chew up the caterpillars and present them to the larvae in a semifluid mass.

So much for the mason wasps, a large complex of Vespidae nearly all of which employ mud in their nests. We think of these as the most primitive vespids, as in many ways they are. But they are well ahead of the digger wasps, only a few of which lay their egg in the empty cell and none of which chew up the prey and feed it directly to the larva. From these mason wasps there apparently arose, a long while ago, a stock that switched from mud to paper. This is not really so big a difference in behavior as it seems. Mason wasps chew a little soil, moisten it with saliva, then plaster it onto the nest. Paper wasps turn to rotten wood, or at least to weathered wood, chew off some of it, macerate it, mix it with saliva, then apply it to the nest in sheets. Some paper wasps make a rather poor grade of paper, while others make a very tough parchment—the wonderful nests of hornets and yellow jackets did not evolve overnight from crude mud nests. Once these wasps had developed the practice of making paper, they radiated into several different groups, most of them tropical and some of them highly successful. The nests of some of these tropical paper wasps are wonderful things to behold. Sometimes there are several types of paper in a single nest, and the architecture is marvelously varied.

Polistes is a fairly good example of a relatively simple paper wasp. In Polistes the prey is always fed to the larva after it is chewed up into a ball. Furthermore, the nests of Polistes are usually founded by several co-operating females, and these females live a much longer time than is the case in the wasps we have considered up to this point. An active Polistes nest is a commune of mothers and daughters working together, and the individuals no longer take care of just their own offspring —they feed any larva that needs food. Certain of the females— the daughters born in the early part of the summer—are smaller than the others and have no opportunity to mate. These constitute a "worker caste" of sorts.

The hornets and yellow jackets show several advances over Polistes. The nests are larger and much more populous, and are surrounded by a protective envelope. The workers construct special, large cells and provision them with more food than usual to produce a crop of queens which are larger and differ to some extent in structure and color from the workers. The next spring each surviving queen founds a colony alone and remains the sole queen in it. The sting is no longer used to any appreciable extent to paralyze the prey but has acquired barbs and become a weapon of colony defense. The bright colors of yellow jackets, incidentally, are not without significance. They are "warning colors," advertising to birds and other predators the fact that these insects are not to be treated as just another morsel of food. There are a good many perfectly harmless flies which "mimic" yellow jackets in color, body form, and to some extent in behavior. Presumably these flies achieve protection from predators by "fooling" them; the birds and other predators have learned to avoid that color pattern.

The venom of wasps, which is respected by lower animals as well as by humans, is a complex material which has never been completely analyzed. Actually its composition differs somewhat in different wasps, and this may account for the fact that the effects of the sting differ in severity and duration in different wasps. In yellow jackets, the three major constituents of the sting are all chemicals which are widely distributed in the animal kingdom and which have important functions in the bodies of most higher animals. These are acetylcholine, serotonin, and histamine. All are classified as hormones, though their function in venom seems to be merely as pain-producers. Histamine is well known for its involvement in allergic reactions, which in some measure can be controlled by the popular drugs known as antihistamines. Some of these same substances, incidentally, occur in the venom of scorpions and even in the stings of jellyfish. A recent study has shown that the stings of nettle are produced by the same three major substances: acetylcholine, serotonin, and histamine. Such is the unity of the natural world!

This brief outline of wasp evolution is full of omissions, as I have concerned myself mostly with the wasps we have considered in this book, omitting many tropical forms which actually add much to the story. Furthermore, an account like this, based as it is entirely upon contemporary wasps, can only present suppositions as to the precise pattern of events many millions of years ago. Yet the broad outlines are fairly evident, and some of our common wasps do suggest some of the levels of complexity which must have characterized the most advanced wasps in past geological periods. The lowly black spider wasp, bumbling over the clods of the garden, is a far cry from a worker yellow jacket, housekeeper, breadwinner, and nursemaid of a great paper domicile hung in a tree. In the tropics there are wasps that have larger and more populous nests, but none that show any real advances over our common Vespulas. The next time yellow jackets descend upon your picnic, remember: You are being joined by true aristocrats.

To a person attuned to them, like myself, the world seems full of wasps. I have never actually counted the species on Wasp Farm, but I would judge there are over one hundred that occur there fairly regularly. Karl Krombein, entomologist of the U. S. Department of Agriculture and one of the world's most noted authorities on wasps, has been making a census of the wasps found on Plummer's Island, a small, fourteen-acre island in the Potomac not far from Washington, D.C. So far, he has recorded over 250 species, and the end is not yet in sight. And some species of wasps are incredibly abundant; I once estimated ten thousand individuals in a large nesting aggregation of a Bembix in southern Florida.

In spite of all this, it must be admitted that most wasps are relatively scarce, that nearly all of them nest rather obscurely, and that none of them make a very important impression upon man or upon the populations of the insects they prey upon. Most wasps seem simply to skim the cream off the abundance of nature, taking a small percentage of the most common of insects. Attempts to manipulate wasps in order to control insect pests have generally ended in failure; the only exception I know of is the case of the "Spanish Jack," a species of Polistes that has been intentionally carried about in the West Indies and has been of some importance in reducing the population of several pests.

Perhaps, then, the story of wasp evolution is the story of a long road to failure. Perhaps the best that can be said for wasps is that at one point early in their history they gave rise to the ants, and at another point somewhat later on to the bees. Ants and bees are certainly not failures by any standards. Ants are probably the most abundant of all creatures on land, and they seem to carry on their manifold activities without being discouraged very much by man; in fact, some species thrive in his homes and gardens. As for the bees, without them we would be without most of the flowering plants, without many of our food crops. No matter what strange things man does to the face of the earth in the future, it is hard to imagine him getting along without bees to pollinate his crops.

We humans, of course, tend to define success in terms of dollars and cents, in terms of how big a "splash" is made in the world, in terms of how much the environment is molded to our ends. But other definitions are possible. If I were to define success as a harmonious living together with the environment, as a gradual unfolding into many small available places in nature, as a surviving for eons of time *without* making a great splash—then the wasps would qualify. But where would that leave man?

Index

HOWARD ENSIGN EVANS is Associate Curator of Insects at the Museum of Comparative Zoology at Harvard University. He received his B.A. degree in Zoology from the University of Connecticut and his M.S. degree (in Entomology) and Ph.D. degree (in Insect Taxonomy) from Cornell University. He has taught previously at Kansas State University and at Cornell. While at Cornell, Dr. Evans and his wife bought an eight-acre farm in Ithaca, where all wasps were made welcome. This book is Dr. Evans' personal account of the lives and behavior of the various wasps which nested there.

Dr. Evans is a member of the Entomological Society of America, the Society for the Study of Evolution, the Society of Systematic Zoology, the American Association for the Advancement of Science, and other organizations. He has written numerous articles for scientific journals as well as *Natural History Magazine, National Parks Magazine,* and *The Explorer,* and a book, *Studies on the Comparative Ethology of Digger Wasps of the Genus Bembix.* He presently lives in Lexington, Massachusetts with his three children and his wife, a trained biologist, who often assists him in his work on wasps.

ANTS

VESPIDAE

TIPHIIDAE

SAWFLIES

WASPS